Everyday Mathematics®

Algorithms Handbook

Grades 2-6

The McGraw-Hill Companies

Cover Credits
©Bonnie Jacobs/iStock International Inc.

Image Credits:
Cover (t)Bonnie Jacobs/iStock International Inc., (cl)Tim Flach/Stone+/Getty Images, (c)John W. Banagan/Iconica/Getty Images, (cr)Pier/Stone/Getty Images, (r)Digital Vision/Getty Images, (b)Estelle Klawitter/CORBIS; **Back Cover** (l)Estelle Klawitter/CORBIS, (cl)Tim Flach/Stone+/Getty Images, (c)John W. Banagan/Iconica/Getty Images, (cr)Pier/Stone/Getty Images, (r)Digital Vision/Getty Images.

www.WrightGroup.com

Printed in The United States of America.

Send all inquiries to:
Wright Group/McGraw-Hill
P.O. Box 812960
Chicago, IL 60681

ISBN 978-0-07-654847-7
MHID 0-07-654847-3

5 6 7 8 9 RHR 13 12 11 10

The McGraw-Hill Companies

Contents

Introduction

In everyday life, an algorithm is any well-defined procedure, method, or routine used to solve a problem. For example, a bread recipe is an algorithm giving the necessary ingredients and cooking procedures to produce the type of loaf you expect every time you bake one. The instructions for operating cell phones, home-security systems, or calculators are all forms of algorithms. As a teacher, you probably establish procedures for students to store their belongings, line up for activities, or use classroom materials, and the authors of the *Everyday Mathematics*® program encourage you to establish other, more mathematical, routines such as keeping a weather record or class calendar.

Yet probably the most familiar procedures in the everyday life of elementary school teachers and students are the pencil-and-paper computational algorithms for adding, subtracting, multiplying, and dividing numbers. There are dozens of computational algorithms that have been used all over the world throughout history: in Babylon and sub-Saharan Africa; in South America and Europe; in ancient Egypt and the United States. Although algorithms can look very different from one another, they are all well-defined, step-by-step procedures that guarantee correct answers using any numbers.

A University of Chicago graduate student once counted 17 addition, 18 subtraction, and 32 multiplication algorithms for whole numbers alone!

What Makes a Good Algorithm?

A good bread recipe is efficient (doesn't have unnecessary steps or ingredients), unambiguous (the instructions aren't vague or confusing), and reliable (unless a mistake is made, the loaf comes out as expected). Likewise, a good computational algorithm is efficient, unambiguous, and reliable in applying a basic arithmetic operation to any two numbers.

A computational algorithm is also good if a student "owns" it, meaning that it makes sense, is easy to remember, and inspires the confidence to use it to solve new, unfamiliar problems. The *Everyday Mathematics*® program promotes such ownership by encouraging students to invent their own algorithms.

Algorithm invention encourages students to use skills they already have, exercise their common sense, and gain new skills and knowledge. Students learn to ask questions that are important in problem solving such as, "How long will this take?" or "Is there a better way?" As students create their own procedures, they also develop persistence and the confidence to solve increasingly difficult problems. Students who invent their own algorithms learn that their intuitive methods are valid and that mathematics makes sense. All these benefits qualify students' invented algorithms as good algorithms.

What Are the Best Algorithms?

Deciding what is best for an individual student and what is best for a community is always a delicate matter, even when it comes to algorithms.

Your Best Algorithms

For you as an individual, the *best* bread recipe depends on your situation: Are you baking the loaf for children or adults; for sandwiches or as soup bowls; in a kitchen or over a campfire? Variations on one recipe, and occasionally a different recipe altogether, can help you meet your different needs.

$$\begin{array}{r} {\scriptstyle 9\,10} \\ 3\not{0}\not{1} \\ -\quad 3 \\ \hline 298 \end{array}$$

"Is all this really necessary?"

Similarly, the *best* computational algorithm depends on the problem to be solved and the capabilities of the problem solver. Hopefully, most people use a mental algorithm to calculate 5 – 3, not a pencil-and-paper one. Calculating 301 – 3 by writing it in the margin and "borrowing" hardly seems to be the best approach. And does it seem best to work from right-to-left to calculate 300 ∗ 20? Unfortunately, students who are taught only one so-called "best" pencil-and-paper algorithm per operation tend to use those algorithms even for these examples. Such students do not use good *number sense.*

People with Good Number Sense

- are flexible in their thinking about numbers and arithmetic and look for "shortcuts" to make their efforts more efficient;
- are continually cultivating good mental-math skills, along with reliable algorithms and procedures for finding results they can't produce mentally;
- can use their number and arithmetic skills to solve problems in everyday situations;
- can recognize unreasonable results when they see numbers in print, in other media, or in their own work.

Students with sound number sense do not automatically categorize a given problem, such as 301 – 3, as an addition or subtraction problem. Instead, they think about the problem and use the operation and algorithm that is most efficient or convenient for solving it. Such students are reflective and creative in their use of the four operations, and they do not blindly use ready-made algorithms as substitutes for thinking and common sense.

To help students develop good number sense, the *Everyday Mathematics*® curriculum shows them a variety of computational algorithms in different problem situations, often challenges them to invent algorithms of their own, and regularly asks them to decide which available algorithm is "best" to perform a given computation.

Our Best Algorithms

Even bread experts can disagree on which recipe is the best. Does the best recipe help bakers learn the principles of making other kinds of breads, or is it best to prepare bakers to make pastries, or to help bakers learn techniques to get into a culinary academy? And even if all the experts agree on one best recipe, can it possibly be best for everyone? For example, to prepare a loaf similar to one prepared by a baker at sea level, a baker at high altitude needs to use less sugar and bake longer or at a higher temperature—circumstances that are beyond the control of the opinions of expert bakers.

Currently in the United States, the traditional algorithms for adding, subtracting, multiplying, and dividing that you probably learned in school are sometimes called the standard algorithms. They are taught in the United States but they are not internationally agreed upon, so the *Everyday Mathematics*® authors refer to those algorithms as the U.S. traditional addition, subtraction, multiplication, and division algorithms.

After years of research and classroom testing, the authors of the *Everyday Mathematics*® program do not think that the U.S. traditional algorithms are the best ones for helping students develop both computational skill and good number sense. To these ends, four Focus Algorithms have been identified that, while being comparably efficient, unambiguous, and reliable to the traditional ones, also offer students richer opportunities to understand the underlying concepts of the operations. Because all students are expected to learn them, they help focus classroom discussions about algorithmic thinking in general. They also serve as the go-to algorithms for students who may not have mastered any other algorithms. For these reasons, the Focus Algorithms are the *Everyday Mathematics*® community's overall "best" algorithms (but, of course, even they may not be the best ones to choose for any given problem).

Yet while the *Everyday Mathematics*® curriculum has its own computational Focus Algorithms, the authors realize that parents and others often insist that students master specific algorithms. Many students learn the U.S. traditional algorithms from siblings or adults at home. Lessons that you can use to teach the traditional algorithms are included in this handbook. In any case, the authors of the *Everyday Mathematics*® program encourage you to do what is best suited to your situation. The program's aim is to help you teach, not to impose ideas or demands on you.

Why Not Just Teach the "Best" Algorithms?

Studying a variety of recipes helps turn beginning bakers into pastry chefs who are able to adapt their baking to accommodate a variety of needs and situations. In a similar way, having several algorithms from which to choose gives students a better opportunity to understand the underlying concepts of the operations and choose whichever procedure works best for them. (Note that while individual students are encouraged to find their own best procedures, the Focus Algorithms [one for each operation] serve as anchors for all students to discuss and master.)

After students have had opportunities to experiment with computation strategies of their own, the *Everyday Mathematics*® program introduces several alternative algorithms for each operation; many algorithms are written, but several model the operations using manipulatives or pictures, providing alternative perspectives to meet the diverse learning styles in your classroom. Some of the alternative algorithms closely resemble methods students are likely to have devised on their own. Others are traditional algorithms used in the United States or in other countries, either currently, or in the past. Still others are simplifications of traditional algorithms or wholly new algorithms that have significant advantages in today's technological world. Collecting alternative algorithms could be a class project, or even one that builds from year to year, helping students to be aware that mathematics, even pencil-and-paper computation, is a continually growing subject.

Pencil-and-Paper Algorithms in the Digital World

Who needs a bread recipe? My local bakery is fantastic!

In July 2008, a new column-addition algorithm developed by a mathematician and a computer scientist was presented at the International Congress of Mathematics Education in Monterrey, Mexico.

In the modern, high-technology world, most adults reach for calculators when faced with any moderately complicated arithmetic computation. This behavior is sensible and should be an option for students, too. Nevertheless, we hope that this introduction helps you better understand how the *Everyday Mathematics*® program gives students opportunities to benefit in many ways from inventing algorithms and learning traditional and alternative non-calculator procedures. *In summary:*

- Students are more motivated when they do not have to memorize traditional paper-and-pencil algorithms without understanding why they work. In fact, most people are more interested in things that they can understand, and students generally understand their own methods, as obscure as they may sometimes be to others.
- Students are better able to maneuver among different mathematical models. They readily translate among manipulatives, oral and written words, pictures, and symbols. The ability to represent a problem in more than one way is important in problem solving.
- Students are more able to transform any given problem into an equivalent, easier problem. For example, 301 – 3 can be transformed to the easier 300 – 2, because taking 1 from both numbers in a subtraction problem does not change the answer.
- Students gain more experience in nonroutine problem solving by devising creative problem-solving strategies and by refining those strategies for use on a more permanent basis. They learn to manage their resources efficiently and build on what they already know. They also develop persistence and confidence in dealing with difficult problems.

And last, but not least, students can have fun with algorithms. Just as a baker can enjoy experimenting with different bread recipes, students can enjoy trying out different computational algorithms. As the great German mathematician and inventor of the calculus Gottfried Wilhelm Leibniz once wrote, "Let us calculate!"

Using the *Algorithms Handbook*

The *Algorithms Handbook* may be used as a supplement to the *Everyday Mathematics*® program. The handbook outlines several of the many possible algorithms for each operation and is based on the *Everyday Mathematics*® belief that because children begin their school years with intuitive mathematics skills, they are quite capable of adapting both traditional and nontraditional algorithms to suit their individual strengths and purposes.

The handbook contains most of the algorithms used and discussed in the *Everyday Mathematics*® materials and a few additional ones as well. Several problems throughout the book feature a Show Me icon (Show Me) which means that a worked example may be found on *everydaymathonline.com.*

For each algorithm, there is a **teaching notes page** on the left and a **student practice page** on the right. The **student practice page** can be made into an instructional transparency or duplicated for each child.

Look for the following features on each teaching notes page:

- a brief description of the algorithm
- an activity designed to help build understanding of the algorithm
- questioning strategies to help you guide your students through the examples
- an "Error Alert" and techniques for dealing with common errors
- suggestions for checking student understanding
- answers to the "Check Your Understanding" exercises on the student practice page

Look for the following features on each student practice page:

- step-by-step directions for following the algorithm
- one or two examples
- "Check Your Understanding" exercises, with problems presented in order of difficulty

Practice Sets

At the back of this handbook (pages 85–184) there are 60 sets of mixed computation practice. There are ten sets for each grade. One problem in each set features a Show Me icon, indicating the presence of a worked example on *everydaymathonline.com.*

The suggested grade level and lesson number are indicated on the teacher answer pages. Naturally, more skilled third graders might benefit from higher-level practice, while less skilled sixth graders might benefit from lower-level practice. Note that the grade-level suggestion for each set is only indicated on the teacher answer page to allow for maximum flexibility and use of student Practice Sets.

Both horizontal and vertical formats are used for the problems on these Practice Set pages. Note that the *Everyday Mathematics*® program uses two symbols for multiplication (× and ∗) and three symbols for division (/ and ÷ and $\overline{)\quad}$). Additionally, the *Everyday Mathematics*® curriculum uses an arrow → for division problems that result in quotients with remainders because, for example, "64 ÷ 7 = 9 R1" is not a true number sentence.

Teaching Notes and Student Pages

Column Division

Column division connects a manipulative-based approach to paper-and-pencil. Making this connection allows students to conceptually understand the division process as they move to the symbolic level. This process encourages students to utilize base-10 blocks and language that breaks the dividend into separate digits. For example, 583 would focus on 5 things, 8 things, and 3 things rather than 583 items. The student breaks each part into hundreds, tens, and ones, with only one place value being considered at a time.

Even those students whose basic-facts knowledge and estimation skills are limited can find correct answers using this approach to division. In the process, students can move from the concrete to the paper-and-pencil level once they feel comfortable. This graphic column presentation greatly reduces error.

Build Understanding

Divide the class into groups of three. Provide each group with base-10 blocks and direct them to model the number 53 (5 tens, 3 ones). Tell students that the blocks represent 50 pieces of candy and direct them to divide the pieces equally among two students. When dividing the 5 longs among 2 students, the groups should see that they have to exchange one long for ten ones. The groups should determine that each student would receive 26 pieces of candy with 1 left over.

The sharing of base-10 blocks at each place value is the conceptual basis for this division algorithm. Explain that it is best to always begin with the largest base-10 blocks. If they can't be shared evenly, they should be exchanged for smaller base-10 blocks, as in the example above.

Using page 71, walk students through an example of the column-division algorithm.

Error Alert Watch for students who do not trade in one of the longs for 10 ones when dividing 53 into 2 groups. Do another example with these students to make sure they understand the process of equal grouping.

Check Understanding

Give each group 2 or 3 additional problems to solve. Encourage each student to explain his or her strategy while working so that the small group can follow along. If many students are confused about a particular aspect of the algorithm, do another problem as a whole class. When you are reasonably certain that most of your students understand the algorithm, assign the "Check Your Understanding" exercises at the bottom of page 71. *(See answers in margin.)*

Page 71 Answer Key

1. 151 R2
2. 121
3. 76
4. 66 R3
5. 208
6. 1,975 R1
7. 1,340 R3
8. 537 R11

Division

Name Date Time

Column Division

In the example below, think of sharing $583 among 4 people.

1. Draw lines to separate the digits in the dividend. Work left to right. Begin in the left column.
2. Think of the 5 in the hundreds column as 5 $100 bills to be shared by 4 people. Each person gets 1 $100 bill. There is 1 $100 bill remaining.
3. Trade the 1 $100 bill for 10 $10 bills. Think of the 8 in the tens column as 8 $10 bills. That makes 10 + 8 = 18 $10 bills in all.
4. If 4 people share 18 $10 bills, each person gets 4 $10 bills. There are 2 $10 bills remaining.
5. Trade the 2 $10 bills for 20 $1 bills. Think of the 3 in the ones column as 3 $1 bills. That makes 20 + 3 = 23 $1 bills.
6. If 4 people share 23 $1 bills, each person gets 5 $1 bills. There are 3 $1 bills remaining.

   Record the answer as 145 R3.
   Each person receives $145 and $3 are left over.

Check Your Understanding

Solve the following problems.

1. 455 ÷ 3	**2.** 726 ÷ 6	**3.** 532 / 7	**4.** 267 / 4
5. 832 / 4	**6.** 3,951 ÷ 2	**7.** 6,703 / 5	**8.** 8,603 / 16

Write your answers on a separate sheet of paper.

Division

Algorithms Correlation Chart

Algorithm	Grade Level	Related Lessons in the *Teacher's Lesson Guide**	Related Pages in the *Student Reference Book*	Online Animations
Addition				
Partial-Sums Addition	**2**	**4-9**, 6-1, **11-1**		✓
	3	**2-7**	Page 57	✓
	4	**2-7**, 5-2	Pages 10, 36	✓
	5	**2-2**	Page 13	✓
	6		Page 13	✓
Column Addition	**3**		Page 59	
	4	**2-7**	Page 11	✓
	5	**2-2**	Page 13	✓
	6		Page 13	✓
U.S. Traditional Addition	**2–4**			✓
	5		Page 14	✓
	6		Page 14	✓
Algorithms for Fraction Addition	**4**	**7-5**		
	5	**5-3, 6-8, 6-9**, 8-3	Page 68	
	6	**4-3**, 7-5	Page 83	
Algorithms for Mixed-Number Addition	**5**	**6-8, 8-2**	Page 70	
	6	**4-4, 4-5**, 4-6	Page 84	
Subtraction				
Partial-Differences Subtraction	**2, 3**			✓
	4	**2-9**	Page 15	✓
	5	**2-3**	Page 17	✓
	6		Page 17	
Counting-Up Subtraction	**2**	**6-5, 11-2**	Page 33	✓
	3	**2-8**, 4-5	Page 63	✓
	4	**2-6**, 2-9	Pages 14, 37	✓
	5		Page 16	
	6		Pages 16, 33	✓
U.S. Traditional Subtraction	**2**		Page 31	✓
	3–6			✓
Trade-First Subtraction	**2**	**11-3**, 12-4	Page 35	✓
	3	2-5, **2-8**	Pages 60, 61	✓
	4	**2-9**	Pages 12, 36	✓
	5	**2-3**	Pages 15, 35	

*** Bold indicates Part 1 of lesson.**

Algorithms Correlation Chart

Algorithm	Grade Level	Related Lessons in the *Teacher's Lesson Guide**	Related Pages in the *Student Reference Book*	Online Animations
Subtraction				
Fraction Subtraction	4	**7-5**		
	5	**6-8, 6-9**	Page 68	
	6	**4-3**	Page 83	
Mixed Numbers	5	**6-8, 8-3**	Page 71	
	6	**4-4, 4-5,** 4-6	Page 85	
Multiplication				
Partial-Products Multiplication	3	**9-4,** 9-6, 9-9, **9-11,** 9-12	Pages 68, 69	✓
	4	**5-5, 5-6, 9-8**	Page 18	✓
	5	**2-8**	Page 19	✓
Lattice Multiplication	3	**9-9,** 9-11, 9-12	Pages 70, 71	✓
	4	**5-7, 9-8**	Page 19	✓
	5	2-8, **2-9**	Pages 20, 40	✓
	6	**2-6**	Pages 20, 39	✓
U.S. Traditional Multiplication	3–6			✓
Fraction Multiplication	5	**8-5, 8-6, 8-7**	Page 76	
	6	**4-6,** 4-10, **6-1**	Page 89	
Mixed-Number Multiplication	5	**8-12**	Page 77	
	6	**4-7,** 4-10, **6-1**	Page 90	
Division				
Partial-Quotients Division	4	**6-3, 6-10, 9-9**	Pages 22, 23	✓
	5	**4-2, 4-4, 4-5, 4-6,** 5-7	Pages 22, 23	✓
	6	**2-7, 2-8,** 3-3, 6-12, 8-2, 9-1	Pages 22, 23	✓
Column Division	5	4-5	Pages 24, 44	
	6	2-7	Page 24	
Fraction Division	5	**8-12**	Pages 79, 80	
	6	**6-2**	Page 91	
Mixed-Number Division	6	**6-2**	Page 93	

* **Bold indicates Part 1 of lesson.**

Partial-Sums Addition

Partial-sums addition is particularly useful for adding multidigit numbers. As the name suggests, a person using this algorithm first calculates partial sums, working one place-value column at a time, and then adds all the partial sums to find the total sum.

The partial sums are easier numbers to work with, and students feel empowered when they discover that, with practice, they can use this algorithm to add numbers mentally.

Build Understanding

Tell students that one way to add larger numbers is to add them one place-value column at a time. Write the number 3,714 on the board. Have a volunteer come to the board and separate the place-value columns in the number by drawing lines between the digits. Then direct another student to write letter abbreviations (Th, H, T, and O) above the digits to show the value of each place.

Using page 5, explain that with this method of adding, the numbers will be added one place-value at a time. Although the columns can be added in any order, working from left to right—that is, from the greatest place value to the least—is the usual procedure. Use questions like the following to guide students through the examples:

- What is the greatest place value in the top (or the greater) addend?
- What is the second-greatest place value in that addend?
- Does each addend have a digit in the (hundreds) place?
- Where is the plus sign written for the partial sums? *(next to the last partial sum)*

Explain the addition in Example 1 in this way: 8 hundreds plus 2 hundreds are 10 hundreds; 800 plus 200 is 1,000 (and so on). Modeling this kind of place-value language for students while working through the examples—and encouraging students to use this language as well—help emphasize the fact that students are adding partial sums before finding the total sum.

Error Alert In Example 1, if students seem confused about which number is the total of 835 and 243, review the meaning of the word "partial." Make sure students understand that each number written below the problem and between the lines represents a part of the final sum. The final sum or total is written below the second line.

Check Understanding

Write 719 + 503 on the board. Have two volunteers demonstrate the computation for this problem using the partial-sums algorithm. Invite one student to write and the other to narrate. Use additional examples if necessary. When you are reasonably certain that most of your students understand the algorithm, assign the "Check Your Understanding" exercises at the bottom of page 5. For practice of more difficult problems, refer students to pages 6–7. *(See answers in margin.)*

Page 5 Answer Key

1. 782

2. 1,274

3. 1,781

4. 1,108

5. 1,668

6. 1,046

7. 3,332

8. 4,784

Page 6 Answer Key

1. 5,555

2. 5,649

3. 9,991

4. 11,684

5. 6,692

6. 15,618

7. 26,376

8. 21,627

Page 7 Answer Key

1. 58,405

2. 80,427

3. 165,838

4. 83,767

5. 116,384

6. 117,488

7. 340,211

8. 146,173

Name Date Time

Partial-Sums Addition

FOCUS ALGORITHM

Addition

Add one place-value column at a time.
Write each partial sum below the problem.
Then add all the partial sums to find the final sum.

Example 1

				835
				+ 243
Add the hundreds.	→	*(800 + 200)*	→	1,000
Add the tens.	→	*(30 + 40)*	→	70
Add the ones.	→	*(5 + 3)*	→	+ 8
Add the partial sums.	→	*(1,000 + 70 + 8)*	→	**1,078**

Example 2

				945
				+ 468
Add the hundreds.	→	*(900 + 400)*	→	1,300
Add the tens.	→	*(40 + 60)*	→	100
Add the ones.	→	*(5 + 8)*	→	+ 13
Add the partial sums.	→	*(1,300 + 100 + 13)*	→	**1,413**

Check Your Understanding

Solve the following problems.

1. 405 + 377

2. 811 + 463

3. 931 + 850

4. 809 + 299

5. 912 + 756

6. 257 + 789

7. 3,098 + 234

8. 4,078 + 706

Write your answers on a separate sheet of paper.

Name Date Time

FOCUS ALGORITHM

Partial-Sums Addition

Add one place-value column at a time.
Write each partial sum below the problem.
Then add all the partial sums to find the final sum.

Addition

Example 1 Show Me

				6,089
				+ 7,825
Add the thousands.	→	*(6,000 + 7,000)*	→	13,000
Add the hundreds.	→	*(0 + 800)*	→	800
Add the tens.	→	*(80 + 20)*	→	100
Add the ones.	→	*(9 + 5)*	→	+ 14
Add the partial sums.	→	*(13,000 + 800 + 100 + 14)*	→	**13,914**

Example 2

				9,838
				+ 7,399
Add the thousands.	→	*(9,000 + 7,000)*	→	16,000
Add the hundreds.	→	*(800 + 300)*	→	1,100
Add the tens.	→	*(30 + 90)*	→	120
Add the ones.	→	*(8 + 9)*	→	+ 17
Add the partial sums.	→	*(16,000 + 1,100 + 120 + 17)*	→	**17,237**

Check Your Understanding

Solve the following problems.

1. 4,397 + 1,158 **2.** 3,066 + 2,583 **3.** 5,932 + 4,059

4. 8,675 + 3,009 **5.** 4,598 + 2,094 **6.** 9,362 + 6,256

7. 23,409 + 2,967 **8.** 9,458 + 5,371 + 6,798

Write your answers on a separate sheet of paper.

Name Date Time

Partial-Sums Addition

FOCUS ALGORITHM

Addition

Add one place-value column at a time.
Write each partial sum below the problem.
Then add all the partial sums to find the final sum.

Example 1

			23,609
			+ 45,984
Add the ten-thousands. →	*(20,000 + 40,000)*	→	60,000
Add the thousands. →	*(3,000 + 5,000)*	→	8,000
Add the hundreds. →	*(600 + 900)*	→	1,500
Add the tens. →	*(0 + 80)*	→	80
Add the ones. →	*(9 + 4)*	→	+ 13
Add the partial sums. →	*(60,000 + 8,000 + 1,500 + 80 + 13)*	→	**69,593**

Example 2

			45,987
			+ 94,421
Add the ten-thousands. →	*(40,000 + 90,000)*	→	130,000
Add the thousands. →	*(5,000 + 4,000)*	→	9,000
Add the hundreds. →	*(900 + 400)*	→	1,300
Add the tens. →	*(80 + 20)*	→	100
Add the ones. →	*(7 + 1)*	→	+ 8
Add the partial sums. →	*(130,000 + 9,000 + 1,300 + 100 + 8)*	→	**140,408**

Check Your Understanding

Solve the following problems.

1. 45,896 + 12,509 **2.** 56,982 + 23,445 **3.** 98,456 + 67,382

4. 65,076 + 18,691 **5.** 74,375 + 42,009 **6.** 29,855 + 87,633

7. 34,429 + 305,782 **8.** 19,568 + 39,537 + 87,068

Write your answers on a separate sheet of paper.

U.S. Traditional Addition (Standard)

U.S. traditional addition (standard) is familiar to most adults and many children. A person using this algorithm adds from right to left, one place-value column at a time, regrouping as necessary.

The traditional method for teaching this algorithm is to begin with concrete models (such as base-10 blocks), using them to demonstrate the regrouping process.

Build Understanding

Divide the class into small groups, pass out place-value blocks to each group, and have each group model the number 117. When all groups have set up their models correctly, tell them to add 6 to the number they have built. If necessary, remind students to regroup the 7 original ones and the 6 new ones into ones and tens. Check each group's final model.

Using page 9, explain that with this method of adding, students will begin on the right with the ones and then move one place-value column at a time to the left. Use questions like the following to guide students through the example:

- What do you have to do when you add 6 ones and 9 ones? *(Trade 10 ones for 1 ten.)*
- What do you have to do when you add 1 ten and 1 ten and 9 tens? *(Trade 10 tens for 1 hundred.)*
- In the diagram or model that represents the sum, what has changed from the two models above it? *(The blocks from the two previous models have been combined to show the regrouping, or the trading, that has taken place.)*

Error Alert Watch for students who do not align addends and sums correctly, because misalignment can lead to incorrect regrouping and wrong answers. Encourage students to allow themselves plenty of room to write the problems out. If necessary, tell students to put a pencil width of space between each digit, or have students write the problems on grid paper.

Check Understanding

Write 329 + 584 on the board. Have a volunteer explain how to solve the problem. Question the student's choices if necessary, but do not write anything on the board unless the student directs you to. Allow the volunteer to solicit help if necessary. When you are reasonably certain that most of your students understand the algorithm, assign the "Check Your Understanding" exercises at the bottom of page 9. *(See answers in margin.)*

Page 9 Answer Key

1. 417

2. 876

3. 903

4. 1,320

5. 1,024

6. 454

7. 8,043

8. 7,433

Name Date Time

U.S. Traditional Addition (Standard)

Use blocks to model the problem. Add from right to left. Then find the total.

Example

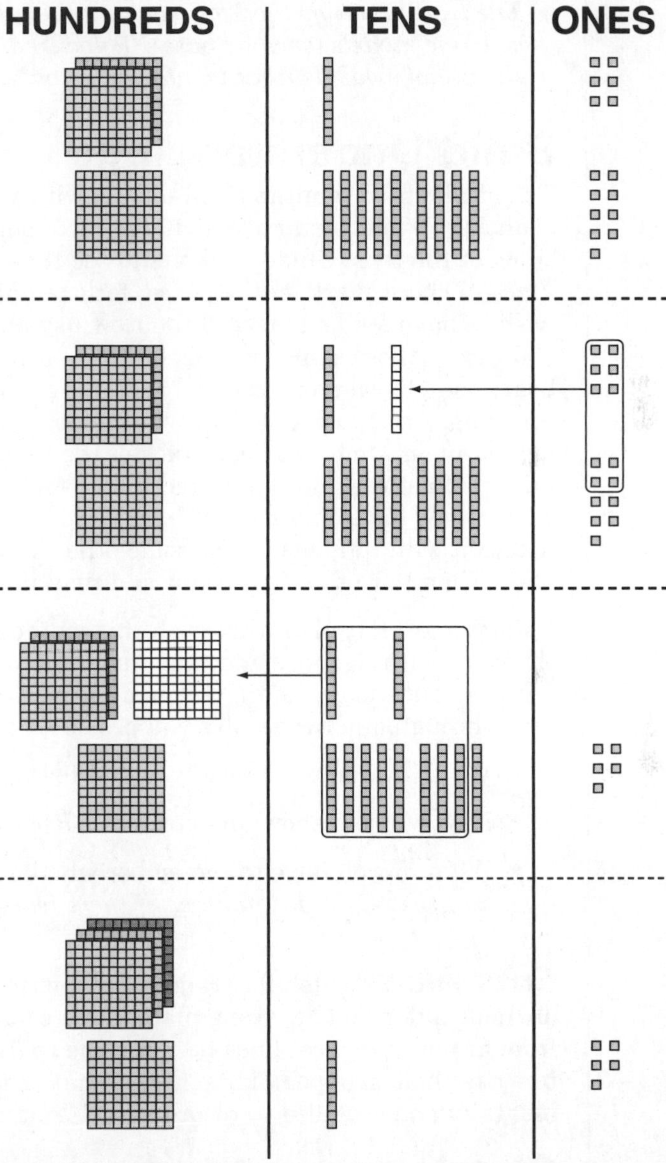

	HUNDREDS	TENS	ONES	
				216 + 199
Add the ones. Trade 10 ones for 1 ten.				1 216 + 199 5
Add the tens. Trade 10 tens for 1 hundred.				1 1 216 + 199 15
Add the hundreds. **415** is the total.				1 1 216 + 199 415

Check Your Understanding

Solve the following problems.

1. 341 + 76

2. 509 + 367

3. 92 + 811

4. 733 + 587

5. 936 + 88

6. 269 + 185

7. 3,968 + 4,075

8. 4,172 + 1,693 + 1,568

Write your answers on a separate sheet of paper.

U.S. Traditional Addition (Standard)

U.S. traditional addition (standard) is familiar to most adults and many children. A person using this algorithm adds from right to left, one place-value column at a time, regrouping as necessary.

The traditional method for teaching this algorithm is to begin with concrete models (such as base-10 blocks) and then gradually move toward the use of symbols (that is, numerals) only.

Build Understanding

Tell students to count to 54 in unison with you on their fingers. Begin counting. When you arrive at 11, ask students how they think they might keep track of the tens. Guide students to see that they will need a mark of some kind—a check mark on the board, for example—for each set of ten. (You might wish to have students record their own symbols on paper at their desks while you record those same symbols on the board.) Place one check mark on the board to help everyone remember that you have 1 ten already. Then continue counting. At 21, ask the class what to do. Guide students to continue using the agreed-upon symbol to keep track of the tens. At 54, ask students how they might adjust the notation to record the fact that they do not have another set of ten; they have only a set of four. Guide students to complete their symbolic notation with tally marks (or some other kind of marks) to stand for the 4 ones. Then have the class count and read its "number" (✔✔✔✔✔////) in unison.

Using page 11, explain that with this method of adding, students will begin on the right with the ones and then move one place-value column at a time to the left. Use questions like the following to guide students through the example (and through other examples you provide):

- Which two numbers will you add first? *(the ones)*
- How will you show an extra ten? *(Record a 1 over the tens place.)*
- What do you have to remember when adding a column of numbers? *(to add the regrouped number, if there is one, along with the other numbers in that column)*

Error Alert Watch for students who write the regrouped ten (or hundred or thousand) over the wrong place-value column. Some students may benefit from drawing vertical lines between the columns so that they can track where to write the regrouped digits. Other students may be able to do the regrouping mentally and not need to record visual "reminders."

Check Understanding

Have a student make up a problem that he or she considers easy and write it on the board. Then ask a volunteer to come to the board, solve the problem, and explain the solution process. Work through as many problems as you feel are necessary, until you are reasonably certain that most of your students understand the algorithm. Then assign the "Check Your Understanding" exercises at the bottom of page 11. *(See answers in margin.)*

Page 11 Answer Key

1. 601

2. 938

3. 955

4. 523

5. 811

6. 8,658

7. 4,620

8. 16,275

Name Date Time

U.S. Traditional Addition (Standard)

Begin adding on the right, and then move to the left. Regroup each partial answer, if necessary, by writing each digit in the appropriate place-value column.

Addition

Example Show Me

```
  398
+ 427
-----
```

Add the ones. *(8 ones + 7 ones = 15 ones)*
Regroup. *(15 ones = 1 ten + 5 ones)* →

```
   1
  398
+ 427
-----
    5
```

Add the tens. *(1 ten + 9 tens + 2 tens = 12 tens)*
Regroup. *(12 tens = 1 hundred + 2 tens)* →

```
  11
  398
+ 427
-----
   25
```

Add the hundreds. *(1 hundred + 3 hundreds + 4 hundreds = 8 hundreds)* →

```
  11
  398
+ 427
-----
  825
```

825 is the total.

Check Your Understanding

Solve the following problems.

1. 582 + 19
2. 748 + 190
3. 856 + 99
4. 307 + 216
5. 236 + 575
6. 8,163 + 495
7. 2,641 + 1,979
8. 5,219 + 3,487 + 7,569

Write your answers on a separate sheet of paper.

Column Addition

Addition

Column addition allows people to work with the place-value columns in any order. It also allows them to write both digits of each partial answer directly underneath the appropriate column and then, if necessary, to go back and adjust the partial answers to find the final answer.

Many students find this algorithm very natural—and instructive.

Build Understanding

Using page 13, explain that with this method of adding, students will add the digits in each column in any order, write individual place-value answers as they go, and then, if necessary, go back and adjust those partial answers to find the final answer. Use questions like the following to guide students through the examples:

- Which two numbers will you begin with? *(It doesn't matter. The columns can be added in any order.)*
- Where do you write the sum for each column? *(in the same column directly beneath the digits being added)*
- How do you adjust the place-value answers? *(If the sum in a column has two digits, write down the ones digit and add a 1 to the answer in the column to the left.)*

While working through Example 1, model appropriate place-value language: "2 hundreds plus 4 hundreds are 6 hundreds; 6 tens plus 8 tens are 14 tens; and 8 ones plus 3 ones are 11 ones. ... Now, we have 14 tens and since 10 tens equal 1 hundred, we have 7 hundreds and 4 tens. ... We have 11 ones and since 10 ones equal 1 ten, we have 5 tens and 1 one." (When working through Example 2, point out that another name for "14 hundreds" is "1 thousand, 4 hundreds.")

Error Alert To help students organize both their thinking and their writing, encourage them to put extra space between the digits in each addend and to draw vertical lines to separate the place-value columns.

Check Understanding

Make sure students understand that the final sum in Example 1 is 751. If necessary, work through additional examples on the board. When you are reasonably certain that most of your students understand the algorithm, assign the "Check Your Understanding" exercises at the bottom of page 13. *(See answers in margin.)*

Page 13 Answer Key

1. 1,275

2. 821

3. 582

4. 913

5. 1,082

6. 1,152

7. 2,626

8. 8,348

Name Date Time

Column Addition

Add one place-value column at a time. Write each place-value answer directly beneath the problem. Then go back and adjust each place-value answer, if necessary, one column at a time.

Example 1

	2	6	8
	+4	8	3
Add the digits in each column. →	6	14	11
If necessary, adjust the hundreds and the tens. →	7	4	11
If necessary, adjust the tens and the ones. →	**7**	**5**	**1**

Example 2

	9	6	7
	+4	9	5
Add the digits in each column. →	13	15	12
If necessary, adjust the hundreds and the tens. →	14	5	12
If necessary, adjust the tens and the ones. →	**1, 4**	**6**	**2**

Addition

Check Your Understanding

Solve the following problems.

1. 511 + 764 **2.** 703 + 118 **3.** 303 + 279

4. 442 + 471 **5.** 453 + 629 **6.** 862 + 290

7. 1,859 + 767 **8.** 1,095 + 2,817 + 4,436

Write your answers on a separate sheet of paper.

Opposite-Change Rule for Addition

The opposite-change rule says that if a number is added to one addend and that same number is subtracted from the other addend, the sum will be unaffected. And since it is arguably easier to add two addends when one of them ends in one or more zeros, the goal is to adjust both addends so that one of them is changed to the nearest ten (or hundred or thousand).

Students find this algorithm particularly useful when calculating mentally.

Build Understanding

Lead students in a quick, oral review of number pairs that add up to 10. Then expand the review by asking students to identify number pairs that add up to 20, 30, 40, 50, and so on. Point out to students that these larger multiples-of-ten number pairs are based on basic addition facts—for example, the 42 and 8 pair is based on 2 and 8; the 31 and 9 pair is based on 1 and 9; and the 25 and 5 pair is based on 5 and 5. Then reverse the review and test students on multiples-of-ten number pairs based on basic subtraction facts: *What is 40 minus 3? 70 minus 6? 90 minus 8?*

Note: Some students may need to write the basic facts and fact extensions on scratch paper. Others may need to see a demonstration: Display 10 counters and have different students demonstrate how many different subgroup pairings can be made with the ten counters while still maintaining the same total number (10).

Using page 15, explain that with this method of adding, students will be renaming the two addends (and rewriting the problem) one or two times before they finally add—the goal being to adjust both addends so that one of them ends in one or more zeros. Use questions like the following to guide students through the examples:

- Which of the two addends is closer to an even ten (or hundred or thousand)?
- How much will you have to add to (or subtract from) that addend to make it an even ten (or hundred or thousand)?
- What will you have to do to the other addend?
- Do you need to adjust the addends again before you are ready to add them together?

Error Alert Watch for students who adjust one addend "up" or "down" without also adjusting the other addend the opposite way. Explain that students are taking the total value of the two numbers and shifting it around, or redistributing it, between the two addends. To maintain the total value, they cannot add a number to one addend without subtracting that same number from the other addend.

Check Understanding

Divide the class into groups of four, and assign a leader in each group to explain which adjustments took place in each of the examples. Tell group members to direct their questions to their group's leader. When you are reasonably certain that most of your students understand the algorithm, assign the "Check Your Understanding" exercises at the bottom of page 15. *(See answers in margin.)*

Page 15 Answer Key

1. 1,480

2. 912

3. 1,367

4. 4,227

5. 4,540

6. 2,113

7. 5,964

8. 20,600

Name Date Time

Opposite-Change Rule for Addition

Decide which addend is closer to an even 10 (or 100 or 1,000).
Decide how to adjust that addend so that it ends in one or more zeros.
Adjust the other addend in the opposite way.
Rename both addends until you reach your goal.
Then add the two addends together to find their sum.

Example 1

364 (addend)
+ 278 (addend)

First, adjust 364 down (by 2) to 362 and adjust 278 up (by 2) to 280.

362
+ 280

Then, adjust 362 down (by 20) to 342 and adjust 280 up (by 20) to 300.

342
+ 300

Finally, add the two addends together. → **642** (sum)

Example 2

5,261
+ 9,400

First, adjust 9,400 down (by 400) to 9,000 and adjust 5,261 up (by 400) to 5,661.

5,661
+ 9,000

Then add the two addends together. → **14,661**

Check Your Understanding

Solve the following problems.

1. 504 + 976 **2.** 642 + 270 **3.** 823 + 544

4. 4,132 + 95 **5.** 972 + 3,568 **6.** 1,477 + 636

7. 2,675 + 3,289 **8.** 14,037 + 6,563

Write your answers on a separate sheet of paper.

Partial-Sums Addition for Decimals

Just as they do with whole numbers, problem solvers add decimals by adding values of digits one place-value column at a time—whether tens or tenths, hundreds or hundredths, and so on. The partial-sums algorithm and the column-addition algorithm used for adding multidigit whole numbers can easily be applied to decimal addition as long as the problem solver is careful to keep track of the place values—both whole-number and decimal place values.

Students will feel empowered as they discover that they can apply their number sense and understanding of whole-number addition to decimal situations. The key, as with whole-number addition, is to pay attention to the place values, and consequently the decimal point, in each of the addends.

Build Understanding

Discuss equivalent decimals like 7.3, 7.30, and 7.300. Then have students annex zeros to find equivalent decimals for 6.7, 0.4, 0.023, and 9. You may also want to review the whole-number versions of this algorithm on pages 4–7.

As you work through Example 1 on page 17, point out that the partial sums should be written with the same number of decimal places as the addend with the greater (or greatest) number of decimal places. Use questions like the following to guide students through the examples:

- Does it matter which place-value column you add first? *(no)*
- In Example 1, why are 6 ones written as 6.000? *(Zeros are added to show the same number of decimal places as the addend with the greater number of decimal places. In this example, both 4.658 and 2.761 happen to have the same number of decimal places—three.)*

Error Alert Watch for students who do not write all the partial sums and the answer with the same number of decimal places. If students have difficulty with this, they may first need to review place value.

Check Understanding

Write 5.298 + 3.44 on the board. Have a volunteer work the problem using the partial-sums algorithm. Encourage the student to "narrate" his or her thought process. Encourage the class to ask questions, and guide the volunteer in answering as necessary. When you are reasonably certain that most of your students understand the algorithm, assign the "Check Your Understanding" exercises at the bottom of page 17. *(See answers in margin.)*

Page 17 Answer Key

1. 6.166

2. 67.84

3. 1.002

4. 0.034

5. 6.291

6. 18.029

7. 102.02

8. 5.914

Name Date Time

Partial-Sums Addition for Decimals

FOCUS ALGORITHM

Addition

Use what you already know about adding whole numbers.
Add one place-value column at a time.
Remember to pay attention to the place values of the addends to record the decimal point in the sum.

Example 1 Show Me

			4.658
			+ 2.761
Add the ones. →	*(4.000 + 2.000)*	→	6.000
Add the tenths. →	*(0.600 + 0.700)*	→	1.300
Add the hundredths. →	*(0.050 + 0.060)*	→	0.110
Add the thousandths. →	*(0.008 + 0.001)*	→	+ 0.009
Add the partial sums. →	*(6.000 + 1.300 + 0.110 + 0.009)*	→	**7.419**

Example 2

			9.682
			+ 1.506
Add the ones. →	*(9.000 + 1.000)*	→	10.000
Add the tenths. →	*(0.600 + 0.500)*	→	1.100
Add the hundredths. →	*(0.080 + 0)*	→	0.080
Add the thousandths. →	*(0.002 + 0.006)*	→	+ 0.008
Add the partial sums. →	*(10.000 + 1.100 + 0.080 + 0.008)*	→	**11.188**

Check Your Understanding

Solve the following problems.

1. 3.441 + 2.725 **2.** 60.45 + 7.39 **3.** 0.906 + 0.096

4. 0.006 + 0.028 **5.** 2.4 + 3.891 **6.** 12.34 + 5.689

7. 89.22 + 12.8 **8.** 5 + 0.034 + 0.88

Write your answers on a separate sheet of paper.

U.S. Traditional Addition for Decimals (Standard)

Addition

U.S. traditional addition for decimals (standard) is familiar to most adults and many children. Those who are proficient in using the standard algorithm with whole numbers should be able to apply their knowledge and skills to decimal situations quite easily. The algorithm and the regrouping process are basically the same. Attention to place value is important because the problem solver always adds the values of digits one place-value column at a time—whether those digits are tens or tenths, hundreds or hundredths, and so on.

Build Understanding

If students need to review the whole-number version of this algorithm, refer them to page 11.

Using page 19, explain that with this method of adding decimals, students will begin by rewriting the problem so that the decimal points of both numbers are vertically aligned. If both addends do not have the same number of decimal places, students will rewrite one of the addends using zeros so that both numbers have the same number of decimal places. You may need to remind students that annexing zeros after the last digit to the right of a decimal point will not change a number's value. Use equivalent fractions, such as $\frac{1}{10} = \frac{10}{100} = \frac{100}{1,000}$, to show students that 0.1 = 0.10 = 0.100.

Students will then add as they would with the standard algorithm for adding whole numbers. Tell students to begin adding on the right and then move to the left one place-value column at a time. Remind students that when digits in a column add up to 10 or more, they will need to regroup. Use questions like the following to guide students through the examples:

- Why must you align the decimal points? *(so that you add ones to ones, tenths to tenths, and so on)*
- In Example 1, what does the 1 written above the 2 stand for? *(1 tenth)*
- In Example 2, why is 1.3 rewritten as 1.300? *(so that both addends will have the same number of decimal places)*
- Where do you put the decimal point in your answer? *(in the same place as the decimal points in the problem)*

Error Alert Watch for students who right-align the numbers, ignoring the position of the decimal point. Also, watch for students who do not include a decimal point in the answer. If it helps students, allow them to draw a vertical line to indicate the position of the decimal point. They write the decimal portion of the answer to the right of the line and the whole-number portion to the left. The line shows students the position of the decimal point in the answer.

Check Understanding

Divide students into pairs and have them solve the problem 4.9 + 3.28. Tell them to write neatly, and then have them exchange papers with their partners. Direct students to check each other's work. If they find a mistake, ask them to circle and identify the mistake. When you are reasonably certain that most of your students understand the algorithm, assign the "Check Your Understanding" exercises at the bottom of page 19. *(See answers in margin.)*

Page 19 Answer Key

1. 13.51

2. 1.72

3. 0.878

4. 2.089

5. 11.08

6. 10.689

7. 1.1758

8. 8.2251

Name Date Time

U.S. Traditional Addition for Decimals (Standard)

Align the addends in a column by place value.
Add from right to left as you would with whole numbers.
Regroup if necessary. Record the decimal point in the sum.

Example 1 

9.23 + 4.29

a. Align the decimal points.
b. Add from right to left.
c. Regroup if necessary.
d. Place the decimal point in your answer.

$$\begin{array}{r} \scriptstyle 1 \\ 9.23 \\ +\ 4.29 \\ \hline 13.52 \end{array}$$

9.23 + 4.29 = 13.52

Example 2 

0.734 + 1.3

a. Align the decimal points.
b. Rewrite 1.3 as 1.300.
c. Add from right to left.
d. Regroup as necessary.
e. Place the decimal point in your answer.

$$\begin{array}{r} \scriptstyle 1 \\ 0.734 \\ +\ 1.300 \\ \hline 2.034 \end{array}$$

0.734 + 1.3 = 2.034

Check Your Understanding

Solve the following problems.

1. 8.32 + 5.19 **2.** 0.23 + 1.49 **3.** 0.386 + 0.492

4. 1.33 + 0.759 **5.** 4.98 + 6.1 **6.** 7 + 3.689

7. 0.53 + 0.6458 **8.** 3.8951 + 4.33

Write your answers on a separate sheet of paper.

Fraction Addition (with Models)

Fraction addition requires a firm understanding of the meaning of a fraction's numerator (the number of fractional parts at hand) and denominator (the number of fractional parts in the whole) as well as facility in naming equivalent fractions.

When adding two or more fractions with like denominators, the problem solver simply adds the numerators or the number of fractional parts in each addend. The denominator that shows the number of fractional parts in the whole does not change.

When adding fractions that have unlike denominators, the problem solver must first rename the addends using a common denominator.

Build Understanding

Review the process of finding common multiples. Have students list a few multiples of 4 *(4, 8, 12, 16, 20, 24)* and 6 *(6, 12, 18, 24, 30, 36)*. Then ask them to circle any numbers that are on both lists. Tell students that the circled numbers are common multiples of 4 and 6. If necessary, have students find common multiples of other number pairs, such as 4 and 10, 6 and 8, and 6 and 9.

Using page 21, explain that when adding fractions with different denominators, students will need to find a common multiple of the denominators, or a common denominator. Then, they will rename these fractions using this common denominator. You may want to explain that renaming fractions will be easier if students use the smallest common denominator. Use questions like the following to guide students through the examples:

- If you add fractions with the same denominator, what do you do to the numerators? *(You add them.)* What do you do to the denominator? *(Nothing. It stays the same.)*
- In Example 2, what is a common denominator of $\frac{1}{3}$ and $\frac{3}{4}$? *(12)*
- To rename $\frac{1}{3}$ with a denominator of 12, which number will you multiply each part of the fraction by? *(4, because $3 * 4 = 12$)*
- To rename $\frac{3}{4}$ with a denominator of 12, which number will you multiply each part of the fraction by? *(3, because $4 * 3 = 12$)*

Error Alert Watch for students who add denominators. If it helps these students, tell them to draw a diagram for each problem. This will help them see the denominator as the number of fractional parts in the *whole*. Also, watch for students who have difficulty finding common denominators. Explain to students that an easy way to find a common denominator of two fractions is to find the product of the two denominators.

Check Understanding

Divide the class into groups of 3 and ask each group to solve the problem $\frac{1}{2} + \frac{2}{5}$. Have one member of the group draw a diagram of the problem. Have the other members use the algorithm. The group members then compare their answers to make sure they are the same. If they are not the same, have the group members correct the error. When you are reasonably certain that most of your students understand the algorithm, assign the "Check Your Understanding" exercises at the bottom of page 21. *(See answers in margin.)*

Page 21 Answer Key

1. $\frac{6}{7}$

2. $\frac{3}{4}$

3. $1\frac{2}{3}$

4. $\frac{7}{12}$

5. $\frac{5}{8}$

6. $\frac{5}{6}$

7. $\frac{17}{24}$

8. $1\frac{1}{24}$

Name Date Time

Fraction Addition (with Models)

Check that the addends have like denominators.
Then add the numerators to find the sum.
The denominator does not change.

Addition

Example 1

$\frac{1}{5} + \frac{3}{5}$

The denominators are the same.

$$\begin{array}{r} \frac{1}{5} \\ + \frac{3}{5} \\ \hline \frac{4}{5} \end{array}$$

Add the numerators.

Example 2

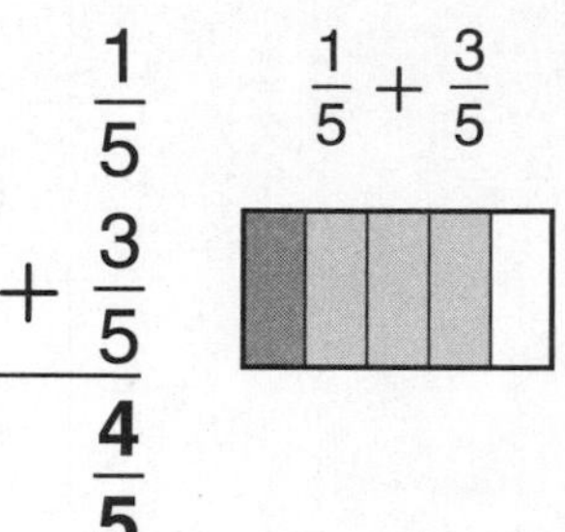

The denominators are not the same.

$$\begin{array}{r} \frac{1}{3} \\ + \frac{3}{4} \\ \hline \end{array}$$

Rename both fractions as equivalent fractions having a common denominator.

$$\begin{array}{r} \frac{1}{3} = \frac{1 * 4}{3 * 4} = \frac{4}{12} \\ + \frac{3}{4} = \frac{3 * 3}{4 * 3} = \frac{9}{12} \\ \hline \frac{13}{12} \end{array}$$

Add the numerators. $\frac{1}{3} + \frac{3}{4} = \frac{13}{12}$, or $1\frac{1}{12}$

Check Your Understanding

Solve the following problems.

1. $\frac{4}{7} + \frac{2}{7}$ **2.** $\frac{1}{8} + \frac{5}{8}$ **3.** $\frac{5}{6} + \frac{5}{6}$ **4.** $\frac{1}{3} + \frac{1}{4}$

5. $\frac{1}{2} + \frac{1}{8}$ **6.** $\frac{2}{3} + \frac{1}{6}$ **7.** $\frac{1}{3} + \frac{3}{8}$ **8.** $\frac{5}{8} + \frac{5}{12}$

Write your answers on a separate sheet of paper.

Mixed-Number Addition (with Models)

Addition

A mixed number names a whole and a fractional part of a whole. For example, the mixed number $3\frac{1}{3}$ names 3 wholes and $\frac{1}{3}$ of another whole.

When adding mixed numbers, some problem solvers prefer to add the whole numbers first and then the fractions. Others choose the reverse—fractions first and then whole numbers.

Build Understanding

If students need to review the algorithm for fraction addition, refer them to page 21.

Demonstrate how to simplify the mixed number $2\frac{7}{4}$. Draw a diagram on the board showing 2 whole circles, 1 circle divided into 4 equal parts, and $\frac{3}{4}$ of a circle. Explain that this drawing shows 2 wholes and 7 fourths. Then write $2 + \frac{4}{4} + \frac{3}{4}$ below the drawings and show that $2 + \frac{4}{4} + \frac{3}{4}$ is equal to $2 + 1 + \frac{3}{4}$, or $3\frac{3}{4}$.

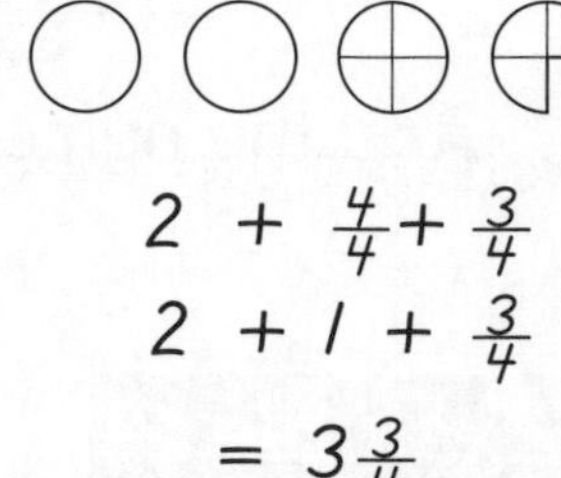

$$2 + \frac{4}{4} + \frac{3}{4}$$
$$2 + 1 + \frac{3}{4}$$
$$= 3\frac{3}{4}$$

Using page 23, explain that students will use their knowledge of fraction addition to solve addition problems having mixed numbers. Then they will rename the sum of each problem if it is not in simplest form. Ask students how the diagram next to $3\frac{6}{4}$ shows the sum of $2\frac{3}{4}$ and $1\frac{3}{4}$. Then have a student explain how the diagram shows that $3\frac{6}{4}$ equals $4\frac{1}{2}$. Use questions like the following to guide students through the examples:

- How do you rename $3\frac{6}{4}$ so that it's in simplest form? *($3\frac{6}{4}$ is equal to $3 + \frac{4}{4} + \frac{2}{4}$, which is equal to $3 + 1 + \frac{2}{4}$, or $4\frac{1}{2}$.)*
- In Example 2, what is a common denominator of $\frac{1}{2}$ and $\frac{2}{3}$? *(6)*
- Does it matter whether you add the whole numbers first or the fractions first? *(no)*

Error Alert Watch for students who, when simplifying a number like $1\frac{9}{5}$, ignore the whole number and give the answer as $1\frac{4}{5}$ instead of $2\frac{4}{5}$. If necessary, assign extra practice exercises in simplifying mixed numbers.

Check Understanding

Divide the class into groups of 3 and ask each group to solve the problem $2\frac{3}{8} + 4\frac{5}{16}$. Have one member of the group draw a diagram to solve the problem. Have the other members use the algorithm. The group members then compare their answers to make sure they are the same. If they are not the same, have the group members correct the error. Circulate around the room checking students' work. When you are reasonably certain that most of your students understand the algorithm, assign the "Check Your Understanding" exercises at the bottom of page 23. *(See answers in margin.)*

Page 23 Answer Key

1. 8

2. $8\frac{2}{5}$

3. $3\frac{1}{2}$

4. $4\frac{5}{6}$

5. $15\frac{11}{16}$

6. $10\frac{3}{10}$

7. $10\frac{17}{24}$

8. $20\frac{17}{36}$

Name Date Time

Mixed-Number Addition (with Models)

One way to add mixed numbers is to add the whole numbers and fractions separately. Check for like denominators before you add the fractional parts. Rename the sum if necessary.

Example 1

$$\begin{array}{r} 2\frac{3}{4} \\ +\,1\frac{3}{4} \\ \hline 3\frac{6}{4} \end{array}$$

Add the fractions and whole numbers.

Rename the sum. $3\frac{6}{4} = 3 + \frac{4}{4} + \frac{2}{4}$

$= 3 + 1 + \frac{2}{4}$

$= 4\frac{2}{4} = \mathbf{4\frac{1}{2}}$

Example 2

$$\begin{array}{r} 3\frac{1}{2} \\ +\,2\frac{2}{3} \\ \hline \end{array}$$

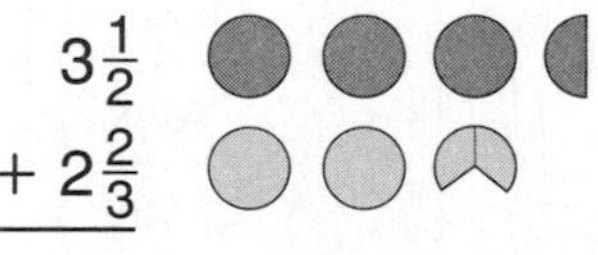

Rename the fractions so that they have a common denominator.

$$\begin{array}{r} 3\frac{3}{6} \\ +\,2\frac{4}{6} \\ \hline 5\frac{7}{6} \end{array}$$

Add the fractions and whole numbers.

Rename the sum. $5\frac{7}{6} = 5 + \frac{6}{6} + \frac{1}{6}$

$= 5 + 1 + \frac{1}{6}$

$= \mathbf{6\frac{1}{6}}$

Check Your Understanding

Solve the following problems.

1. $2\frac{1}{3} + 5\frac{2}{3}$ **2.** $3\frac{4}{5} + 4\frac{3}{5}$ **3.** $1\frac{5}{8} + 1\frac{7}{8}$ **4.** $1\frac{7}{12} + 3\frac{1}{4}$

5. $7\frac{3}{8} + 8\frac{5}{16}$ **6.** $5\frac{1}{2} + 4\frac{4}{5}$ **7.** $6\frac{7}{8} + 3\frac{5}{6}$ **8.** $10\frac{5}{9} + 9\frac{11}{12}$

Write your answers on a separate sheet of paper.

FOCUS ALGORITHM

Trade-First Subtraction

Page 25 Answer Key

1. 11

2. 27

3. 48

4. 28

5. 226

6. 303

7. 59

8. 101

Page 26 Answer Key

1. 19

2. 68

3. 8

4. 231

5. 769

6. 274

7. 673

8. 521

Page 27 Answer Key

1. 24

2. 49

3. 889

4. 687

5. 19

6. 279

7. 1,281

8. 1,893

Trade-first subtraction looks just like the standard algorithm (see pages 28 and 29) when it is completed. The difference is that with the trade-first algorithm, all trading (or regrouping) is carried out before any subtracting begins.

Many students find the trade-first algorithm to be an easy alternative to the switching between trading and subtracting that is required in the traditional algorithm.

Build Understanding

Using pages 25, 26, and 27, explain that with this method of subtracting, students will begin by carrying out all necessary trading until the top number in each column is at least as large as the bottom number. Then students will subtract the numbers in each column (either left-to-right or right-to-left) to find the difference. Use questions like the following to guide students through the examples:

- In the example on page 25, which numbers are in the tens place? *(3 and 7)* Can you remove 7 tens from 3 tens? *(no)* What trade can you make so that you will be able to remove the 7 tens? *(Trade 1 hundred for 10 tens. After trading, there will be 13 tens, and you can then remove 7 tens.)*
- In the example on page 26, what do the 6 and 13 written above the 7 and 3 show? *(They show that 1 of the 7 hundreds was traded for 10 tens, decreasing the number of hundreds to 6 and increasing the number of tens to 13.)*
- In the example on page 27, can you remove the 5 ones without trading? *(No. You must trade to get more ones.)* Can you remove 9 tens from 7 tens? *(No. You must trade 1 hundred for 10 tens, and then trade 1 thousand for 10 hundreds.)*
- Does it matter whether you begin trading and subtracting on the left or on the right? *(no)*

Error Alert Watch for students who simply subtract the lesser number from the greater number in each column, without thought to whether a trade is needed. More work with models can often help these students.

Check Understanding

Have a volunteer go to the board and solve the problem 215 – 196. Ask the volunteer to explain each step as he or she works. The class should direct questions concerning the problem to the volunteer. When you are reasonably certain that most of your students understand the algorithm, assign the "Check Your Understanding" exercises at the bottom of page 25. For practice of simple problems without models, refer students to page 26. For practice of more difficult problems without models, refer students to page 27. *(See answers in margin.)*

Name Date Time

Trade-First Subtraction (with Models)

FOCUS ALGORITHM

Use blocks to model the larger number. Trade blocks between the place-value columns as necessary. Trade until the top number in each column is at least as large as the bottom number. Then subtract the numbers to find the difference.

Example

$$\begin{array}{r} 432 \\ -\ 175 \\ \hline \end{array}$$

Model the larger number (432).

hundreds | tens | ones

1 | 7 | 5

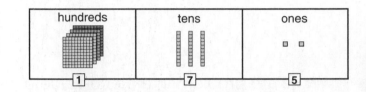

Think: Can I remove 7 tens from 3 tens? (no)

Trade 1 hundred for 10 tens.

1 | 7 | 5

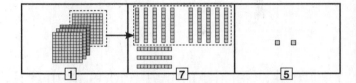

Think: Can I remove 5 ones from 2 ones? (no)

Trade 1 ten for 10 ones.

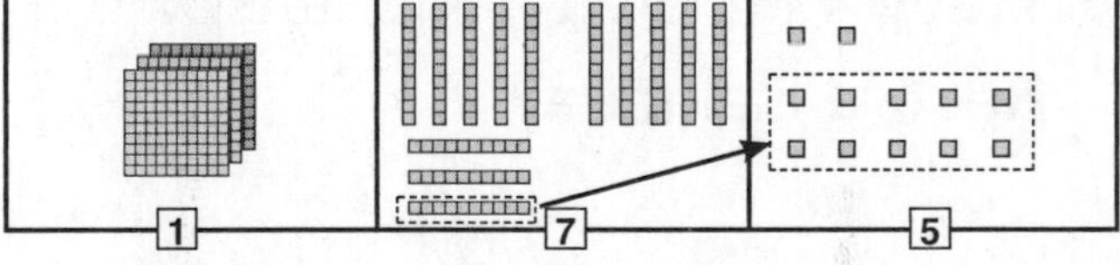

After all the trading, the blocks look like this.

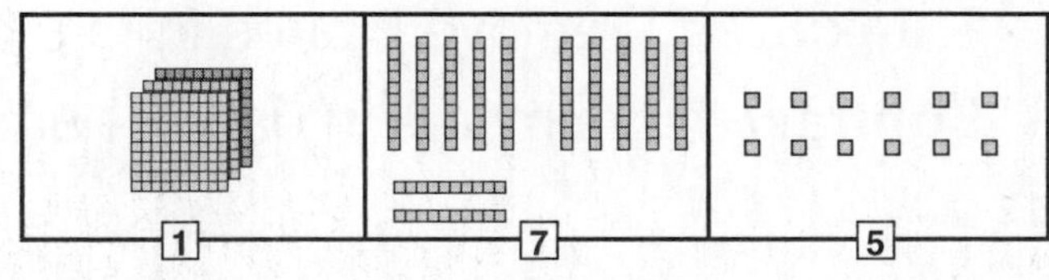

Subtract the numbers in each column.

257 is the difference.

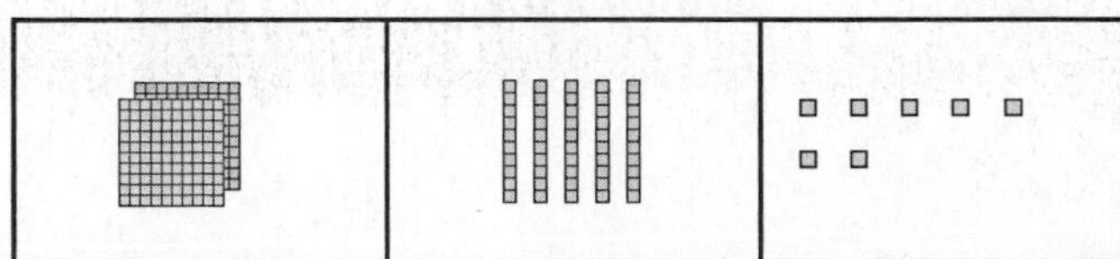

Check Your Understanding

Solve the following problems.

1. 29 − 18 **2.** 61 − 34 **3.** 76 − 28

4. 83 − 55 **5.** 241 − 15 **6.** 322 − 19

7. 115 − 56 **8.** 200 − 99

Write your answers on a separate sheet of paper.

Name Date Time

FOCUS ALGORITHM

Trade-First Subtraction

Look at the numbers in each place-value column. Trade until the top number in each column is at least as large as the bottom number. Then subtract the numbers in each column to find the difference.

Example

$$\begin{array}{r} 738 \\ -\,452 \\ \hline \end{array}$$

Write the problem in a place-value chart.

	100s	10s	1s
	7	3	8
−	4	5	2

Think: Can I remove 5 tens from 3 tens? (no)
Trade 1 hundred for 10 tens.
Record the trade.

	100s	10s	1s
	6	13	
	~~7~~	~~3~~	8
−	4	5	2

Think: Can I remove 2 ones from 8 ones? (yes)
Subtract the numbers in each column.

	100s	10s	1s
	6	13	
	~~7~~	~~3~~	8
−	4	5	2
	2	**8**	**6**

286 is the difference.

Check Your Understanding

Solve the following problems.

1. 51 − 32 **2.** 93 − 25 **3.** 66 − 58

4. 303 − 72 **5.** 831 − 62 **6.** 427 − 153

7. 759 − 86 **8.** 580 − 59

Write your answers on a separate sheet of paper.

Name Date Time

Trade-First Subtraction

FOCUS ALGORITHM

Look at the numbers in each place-value column. Trade until the top number in each column is at least as large as the bottom number. Then subtract the numbers in each column to find the difference.

$$\begin{array}{r} 4{,}471 \\ -\ 1{,}695 \\ \hline \end{array}$$

Example

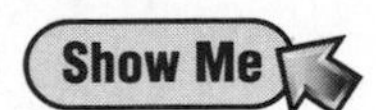

	1,000s	100s	10s	1s
Write the problem in a place-value chart.	4	4	7	1
	− 1	6	9	5
Think: Can I remove 5 ones from 1 one? (no) **Trade** 1 ten for 10 ones. **Record** the trade.	4	4	6 ~~7~~	11 ~~1~~
	− 1	6	9	5
Think: Can I remove 9 tens from 6 tens? (no) **Trade** 1 hundred for 10 tens. **Record** the trade.	4	3 ~~4~~	16 ~~6~~ ~~7~~	11 ~~1~~
	− 1	6	9	5
Think: Can I remove 6 hundreds from 3 hundreds? (no) **Trade** 1 thousand for 10 hundreds. **Record** the trade. **Subtract** the numbers in each column.	3 ~~4~~	13 ~~4~~	16 ~~6~~ ~~7~~	11 ~~1~~
	− 1	6	9	5
2,776 is the difference.	**2**	**7**	**7**	**6**

Check Your Understanding

Solve the following problems.

1. 92 − 68 **2.** 84 − 35 **3.** 938 − 49

4. 782 − 95 **5.** 111 − 92 **6.** 503 − 224

7. 1,340 − 59 **8.** 2,200 − 307

Write your answers on a separate sheet of paper.

Subtraction

U.S. Traditional Subtraction (Standard)

U.S. traditional subtraction (standard) is familiar to most adults and many children. A person using this algorithm subtracts from right to left, one place-value column at a time, regrouping as necessary.

The traditional method for teaching this algorithm is to begin with concrete models (such as base-10 blocks) and then gradually move toward the use of symbols (that is, numerals) only.

Build Understanding

Write the following number on the board (leaving out the comma and adding a fair amount of space between the digits): 28,143. (Fifth and sixth grade students might be ready for a larger number, such as 5,092,411, but, again, be sure to omit all commas and add extra spacing between the digits.) Ask a volunteer to read the number. If the student has difficulty, ask the class what might be done to make the number easier to read. Elicit from students the need for one or more commas, and have another volunteer label each place value with a letter abbreviation (Th, H, T, or O) above each digit.

Using page 29, explain that with this method of subtracting, students will begin with the place value on the far right—the ones. Use questions like the following to guide students through the examples:

- What are the first numbers you will work with? *(the ones)*
- As you study the problem, how many times do you think you will have to rename one of the digits?
- How many digits do you think might be in the answer?

Error Alert Watch for students who write the regrouped number over the correct place-value column but forget to cross out the original number. Keep in mind, however, that some students are able to regroup correctly without the aid of visual reminders.

Check Understanding

Make sure students understand what to do when they need to regroup a place value that is a zero. Write the following problem vertically on the board: 701 − 358. Make sure students understand that they must actually regroup the tens place two times. Have a volunteer work through the problem out loud while you write on the board what the student dictates. When you are reasonably certain that most of your students understand the algorithm, assign the "Check Your Understanding" exercises at the bottom of page 29. *(See answers in margin.)*

Page 29 Answer Key

1. 574

2. 741

3. 266

4. 6,339

5. 4,024

6. 49

7. 22,908

8. 2,746

Name Date Time

U.S. Traditional Subtraction (Standard)

FOCUS ALGORITHM

Start with the ones column, and subtract one column at a time. Regroup (rename) as necessary.

Example 1

Think: Can I subtract 9 ones from 5 ones? (no)

Regroup the 5 tens and 5 ones as 4 tens and 15 ones.

Then **subtract** 9 ones from 15 ones.

```
  4 15
 8 5 5   (5 and 5 crossed out)
-4 3 9
------
 4 1 6
```

Think: Can I subtract 3 tens from 4 tens? (yes)

Subtract 3 tens from 4 tens.

Then **subtract** the hundreds.

416 is the difference.

Example 2

Think: Can I subtract 6 ones from 2 ones? (no)

Regroup the 7 hundreds and 0 tens as 6 hundreds and 10 tens. Then regroup the 10 tens and 2 ones as 9 tens and 12 ones.

Then **subtract** 6 ones from 12 ones.

```
     9
  6 10 12   (10 crossed out)
 7  0  2    (7, 0 and 2 crossed out)
-5  8  6
---------
 1  1  6
```

Think: Can I subtract 8 tens from 9 tens? (yes)

Subtract 8 tens from 9 tens.

Then **subtract** the hundreds.

116 is the difference.

Check Your Understanding

Solve the following problems.

1. 601 – 27 **2.** 815 – 74 **3.** 529 – 263

4. 7,195 – 856 **5.** 9,113 – 5,089 **6.** 1,248 – 1,199

7. 32,084 – 9,176 **8.** 15,643 – 12,897

Write your answers on a separate sheet of paper.

Partial-Differences Subtraction

Partial-differences subtraction builds on a skill most people use daily: reading from left to right. The person using this algorithm begins at the far-left side of the problem and subtracts the subtrahend (the lesser number) from the minuend (the greater number) one place-value column at a time until the final difference between the two numbers is reached.

Most students find it helpful to see the subtrahend expressed in expanded notation, and many students find it natural to move from left to right when performing mathematical operations.

Build Understanding

Review expanded notation: Write 2,638 on the board and explain how to write the number in expanded form (2,000 + 600 + 30 + 8). Have students expand the following numbers at their desks: 318; 1,967; 8,049. Ask volunteers to write the answers on the board, and, if necessary, model a few of the numbers using base-10 blocks.

Note: If students seem confused when one or more of the place values are zero, explain two different ways they can handle the situation: Using 8,049 as an example, students can expand the number either as 8,000 + 0 + 40 + 9 or as 8,000 + 40 + 9.

Using page 31, explain that with this method of subtracting, students will begin on the far-left side of the problem and subtract one place-value column at a time until they find the final difference between the minuend (the top number) and the subtrahend (the bottom number). Use questions like the following to guide students through the example (and through other examples you provide):

- Which number will be broken down into its individual place values? *(the subtrahend)*
- What is the greatest place value in the subtrahend?
- How will you subtract the second-greatest place value in the subtrahend? *(Write it in expanded notation and then subtract it from the minuend.)*
- What is the final difference between the minuend and the subtrahend?

Error Alert Make sure students understand that the second subtracted number (100 in the example on page 31) has been "pulled out" from the original subtrahend. If necessary, have students write each subtrahend in expanded notation and then draw an arrow from each part of the expanded notation to its counterpart in the recorded algorithm (the "solution column").

Check Understanding

Write 213 − 148 on the board. Have three volunteers take turns solving each step of the problem to help emphasize the fact that three place values are being subtracted, one at a time, in sequence. Work through as many problems in this way as necessary until you are reasonably certain that most of your students understand the algorithm. Then assign the "Check Your Understanding" exercises at the bottom of page 31. *(See answers in margin.)*

Page 31 Answer Key

1. 223

2. 566

3. 361

4. 211

5. 6,568

6. 768

7. 42,179

8. 4,449

Name Date Time

Partial-Differences Subtraction

Subtract left to right, one column at a time. In some cases, the larger number is on the bottom. When this happens and you subtract, the difference is a negative number.

Example 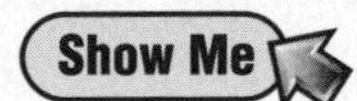

First, write or think of 5,170 as 5,000 + 100 + 70 + 0.

$$\begin{array}{r} 9{,}328 \text{ (minuend)} \\ -\ 5{,}170 \text{ (subtrahend)} \\ \hline \end{array}$$

$$\begin{array}{r} 9{,}328 \\ -\ 5{,}170 \\ \hline \end{array}$$

Subtract the thousands.	→	(9,000 − 5,000)	→	4,000
Subtract the hundreds.	→	(300 − 100)	→	200
Subtract the tens.	→	(20 − 70)	→	− 50
Subtract the ones.	→	(8 − 0)	→	8
Find the total.	→	(4,000 + 200 − 50 + 8)	→	**4,158**

Subtraction

Check Your Understanding

Solve the following problems.

1. 317 − 94 **2.** 582 − 16 **3.** 640 − 279

4. 835 − 624 **5.** 7,104 − 536 **6.** 2,952 − 2,184

7. 43,870 − 1,691 **8.** 15,033 − 10,584

Write your answers on a separate sheet of paper.

Counting-Up Subtraction

Counting-up subtraction is similar to the process of making change: In both processes, the problem solver counts up from the lesser number to the greater number. The person making a purchase counts up from the amount due to the amount tendered. The person using the counting-up algorithm counts up from the subtrahend (the lesser number) to the minuend (the greater number), records each count-up amount, and then totals all the count-up amounts to find the difference between the minuend and the subtrahend.

Build Understanding

Conduct a brief, oral review of number pairs that add up to 10. (You say "4," and students respond "6.") Then work with number pairs that add up to the next-higher multiple of 10. (You say "37," and students respond "3.") Finally, move on to number pairs that add up to the next-higher 100 or 1,000. (You say "52," and students respond "48"; you say "720," and students respond "280.")

Using page 33, explain that with this method of subtracting, students will, in effect, turn a subtraction problem into an addition problem by "counting up" to find the difference between the two numbers in the problem. Use questions like the following to guide students through the examples:

- Which number will you begin counting up from? *(the subtrahend—the lesser number)*
- How much do you need to add to the number to count to the nearest ten? The nearest hundred? The nearest thousand? The minuend?
- How many numbers do you have to add on and add up in all to get from the subtrahend to the minuend?
- What is the difference between the subtrahend and the minuend?

Error Alert Watch for students who forget how high to count. Remind students that they are to count up only to the greater number in the problem. If it helps them, have students circle the greater number to remind themselves when to stop!

Check Understanding

Divide the class into small groups, and give a different problem to each group: 811 − 609; 335 − 271; 495 − 184; 241 − 39; 572 − 399; 614 − 255. Have each student in each group use the counting-up algorithm to find the solution to his or her group's problem. Then encourage group members to talk the problem through together. If time allows, have one volunteer from each group explain his or her group's solution to the class. Finally, when you are reasonably certain that most of your students understand the algorithm, assign the "Check Your Understanding" exercises at the bottom of page 33. *(See answers in margin.)*

Page 33 Answer Key

1. 183

2. 175

3. 177

4. 1,169

5. 2,603

6. 6,437

7. 3,780

8. 4,385

Name Date Time

Counting-Up Subtraction

Start with the subtrahend and decide by how much you want to count up first. Count up, recording the "count-up" amount. Continue counting up until you reach the minuend. Then, to find the difference between the subtrahend and the minuend, find the total of all the count-up amounts.

Example 1

$$\begin{array}{r} 729 \\ -\ 518 \\ \hline \end{array}$$

Count up from 518 to 729. → + 2 → 520
+ 80 → 600
+ 100 → 700
Then total all the count-up amounts. + 29 → 729
211 is the difference. **211**

Example 2

$$\begin{array}{r} 9{,}438 \\ -\ 8{,}167 \\ \hline \end{array}$$

Count up from 8,167 to 9,438. → + 3 → 8,167
+ 30 → 8,170
+ 800 → 8,200
Then total all the count-up amounts. + 438 → 9,000
1,271 is the difference. **1,271** 9,438

Check Your Understanding

Solve the following problems.

1. 814 − 631 **2.** 197 − 22 **3.** 555 − 378

4. 6,097 − 4,928 **5.** 7,112 − 4,509 **6.** 8,836 − 2,399

7. 93,744 − 89,964 **8.** 10,115 − 5,730

Write your answers on a separate sheet of paper.

Trade-First Subtraction for Decimals

Trade-first subtraction for whole numbers can easily be applied to the subtraction of decimals. It looks just like the standard algorithm for decimal subtraction (pages 36–37) when it is completed. The difference is that with the trade-first algorithm, all trading is carried out before any subtracting begins.

Build Understanding

If students need to review the whole-number version of this algorithm, refer them to pages 25–27.

Using page 35, explain that with this method of subtracting decimals, students will begin by writing the problem so that the decimal points are aligned vertically. If the subtrahend and the minuend do not have the same number of decimal places, students will add one or more zeros to the end of one of the numbers so that both numbers have the same number of decimal places.

Students then carry out all necessary trading until the top number in each column is at least as large as the bottom number. Finally, students will subtract the numbers in each column. Use questions like the following to guide students through the examples:

- In the example, which numbers are in the tenths place? *(2 and 7)* Can you remove 7 tenths from 2 tenths? *(no)* What trade can you make so that you will be able to remove the 7 tenths? *(Trade 1 one for 10 tenths. After trading, there will be 12 tenths, and you can then remove 7 tenths.)*
- What do the 5 and 12 written above the 6 and 2 show? *(They show that 1 of the 6 ones was traded for 10 tenths, decreasing the number of ones to 5 and increasing the number of tenths to 12.)*
- Does it matter whether you begin trading and subtracting on the left or the right? *(no)*

Error Alert Watch for students who have difficulty subtracting a decimal from a whole number. If it helps students, ask them to draw vertical lines to separate the place-value columns and write place-value abbreviations (100s, 10s, 1s, 0.1s, 0.01s, 0.001s) above the columns. Making the line that separates the ones (1s) and the tenths (0.1s) columns thicker might also help students accurately place the decimal point in the answer.

Check Understanding

Have a volunteer go to the board and solve the problem 8 − 3.14. Ask the volunteer to explain each step as he or she works. The class should direct questions concerning the problem to the volunteer. When you are reasonably certain that most of your students understand the algorithm, assign the "Check Your Understanding" exercises at the bottom of page 35. *(See answers in margin.)*

Page 35 Answer Key

1. 4.4

2. 1.2

3. 1.82

4. 2.57

5. 0.87

6. 5.449

7. 0.11

8. 8.992

Subtraction

Name Date Time

Trade-First Subtraction for Decimals

FOCUS ALGORITHM

Use what you already know about subtracting whole numbers. Pay attention to the place values of the minuend and subtrahend when you place the decimal point in the difference.

Example

Write the problem in a place-value chart.

$$\begin{array}{r} 6.21 \text{ (minuend)} \\ -\ 2.75 \text{ (subtrahend)} \\ \hline \end{array}$$

Think: Can I remove 7 tenths from 2 tenths? (no)

1s	0.1s	0.01s
6.	2	1
− 2.	7	5

Trade 1 one for 10 tenths.

1s	0.1s	0.01s
5	12	
~~6~~.	~~2~~	1
− 2.	7	5

Think: Can I remove 5 hundredths from 1 hundredth? (no)
Trade 1 tenth for 10 hundredths.

1s	0.1s	0.01s
	11	
5	~~12~~	11
~~6~~.	~~2~~	~~1~~
− 2.	7	5

Subtract the numbers in each column.

1s	0.1s	0.01s
3.	**4**	**6**

3.46 is the difference. **3.46**

Subtraction

Check Your Understanding

Solve the following problems.

1. 6.3 − 1.9 **2.** 3.1 − 1.9 **3.** 6.82 − 5

4. 4.37 − 1.8 **5.** 2 − 1.13 **6.** 5.81 − 0.361

7. 1.1 − 0.99 **8.** 9 − 0.008

Write your answers on a separate sheet of paper.

U.S. Traditional Subtraction for Decimals (Standard)

U.S. traditional subtraction for decimals (standard) is familiar to most adults and many children. Those who are proficient in using the standard algorithm with whole numbers should be able to apply their knowledge and skills to decimal situations quite easily. The algorithm and the regrouping process are basically the same. Attention to place value is important because the problem solver always subtracts the values of digits one place-value column at a time—whether those digits are tens or tenths, hundreds or hundredths, and so on.

Build Understanding

If students need to review the whole-number version of this algorithm, refer them to page 29.

Using page 37, explain that with this method of subtracting decimals, students will begin by writing the problem so that the decimal points are aligned. Then, if the subtrahend and the minuend do not have the same number of decimal places, students will write zeros at the right so that all numbers have the same number of decimal places.

Students will then subtract as they would with the standard algorithm for subtracting whole numbers. Tell students to begin subtracting on the right and then move one place-value column at a time to the left. Remind students that when they cannot subtract a digit from the one above it, they will need to regroup. Use questions like the following to guide students through the examples:

- In Example 1, what do the 4 and 17 written above the 57 show? *(They show that 57 has been regrouped as 4 tenths and 17 hundredths.)*
- In Example 2, why is 12.7 rewritten as 12.700? *(so that the minuend has the same number of decimal places as the subtrahend)*
- Where do you put the decimal point in your answer? *(in the same place as the decimal points in the problem)*

Error Alert Watch for students who have difficulty subtracting a decimal from a whole number. Some students have no difficulty writing zeros to the right of a number such as 1.3, but do not see 4 as 4.0 or 4.00. If it helps students, ask them to draw vertical lines to separate the place-value columns and have them write place-value abbreviations (100s, 10s, 1s, 0.1s, 0.01s, 0.001s) above the columns. Making the line that separates the ones (1s) and the tenths (0.1s) columns thicker might also help students know where to place the decimal point in the answer.

Check Understanding

Have a volunteer go to the board and solve the problem $7.1 - 0.71$. Encourage the student to explain what he or she is doing while working so that the class can follow along. Have students direct their questions to the volunteer, and guide that student in answering as necessary. Repeat the process with $6 - 0.66$. When you are reasonably certain that most of your students understand the algorithm, assign the "Check Your Understanding" exercises at the bottom of page 37. *(See answers in margin.)*

Page 37 Answer Key

1. 0.4

2. 0.793

3. 3.75

4. 6.36

5. 3.05

6. 0.5

7. 0.79

8. 7.001

Name Date Time

U.S. Traditional Subtraction for Decimals (Standard)

Check to make sure that the numbers are aligned in columns by place value. Subtract from right to left, regrouping if necessary, as you would with whole numbers. Record the decimal point in the difference.

Example 1

0.57 − 0.38

Align the decimal points.

Subtract as you would when subtracting whole numbers from right to left.

Regroup as necessary.

Place the decimal point in your answer.

```
   4 17
 0.5̸ 7̸
− 0.3 8
 0.1 9
```

Example 2

12.7 − 1.528

Align the decimal points.

Rewrite 12.7 as 12.700.

Subtract as you would when subtracting whole numbers from right to left.

Regroup as necessary.

Place the decimal point in your answer.

```
        9
      6 1̸0̸ 10
 12.7̸ 0̸ 0
−  1.5 2 8
 11.1 7 2
```

Subtraction

Check Your Understanding

Solve the following problems.

1. 7.2 − 6.8 **2.** 0.854 − 0.061 **3.** 7.85 − 4.1

4. 11.36 − 5 **5.** 6.2 − 3.15 **6.** 3 − 2.5

7. 11 − 10.21 **8.** 8 − 0.999

Write your answers on a separate sheet of paper.

Fraction Subtraction (with Models)

Subtracting fractions requires a firm understanding of the meaning of a fraction's numerator (the number of fractional parts at hand) and denominator (the number of fractional parts in the whole) as well as facility in naming equivalent fractions. When two or more fractions have like denominators, the problem solver subtracts the numerators: that is, the problem solver subtracts the number of fractional parts at hand. The number of fractional parts in the whole—the denominator—does not change.

As is the case with adding fractions, subtracting fractions that have unlike denominators requires an additional step. The problem solver must first rename the fractions so that they have like denominators.

Build Understanding

Review the process of finding common multiples and common denominators. Ask students to find common denominators for problems like $\frac{5}{6} - \frac{1}{3}$ and $\frac{3}{4} - \frac{2}{3}$.

Using page 39, explain that when subtracting fractions with different denominators, students will need to find a common multiple of the denominators, or a common denominator. Then, they will rename the fractions as equivalent fractions having common denominators. Remind students that renaming fractions will be easier if they use the smallest common denominator. Use questions like the following to guide students through the examples:

- To subtract fractions having the same denominator, what do you do to the numerators? *(You subtract them.)* What do you do to the denominator? *(Nothing. It stays the same.)*
- In Example 2, what is a common denominator of $\frac{5}{6}$ and $\frac{1}{4}$? *(12)*
- When renaming $\frac{5}{6}$ so that it has a denominator of 12, which number will you multiply by the denominator? *(2, because $6 * 2 = 12$)*

Error Alert Watch for students who multiply incorrectly when they find common denominators. Stress the need to multiply both the numerator and the denominator by the same number.

Check Understanding

Divide the class into groups of 3 and ask each group to solve the problem $\frac{1}{2} - \frac{3}{10}$. Have one member of the group draw a diagram of the problem. Have the other members use the algorithm. The group members then compare the answers to make sure they are the same. If they are not the same, have the group members correct the error. Circulate around the room checking students' work. When you are reasonably certain that most of your students understand the algorithm, assign the "Check Your Understanding" exercises at the bottom of page 39. *(See answers in margin.)*

Page 39 Answer Key

1. $\frac{2}{5}$
2. $\frac{1}{2}$
3. $\frac{2}{9}$
4. $\frac{5}{12}$
5. $\frac{1}{8}$
6. $\frac{1}{2}$
7. $\frac{1}{24}$
8. $\frac{1}{48}$

Name Date Time

Fraction Subtraction (with Models)

Check that the addends have like denominators.
Then subtract the numerators to find the difference.
The denominator does not change.

Example 1

The denominators are the same.

Subtract the numerators.

$$\begin{array}{r} \frac{6}{7} \\ -\ \frac{2}{7} \\ \hline \frac{4}{7} \end{array}$$

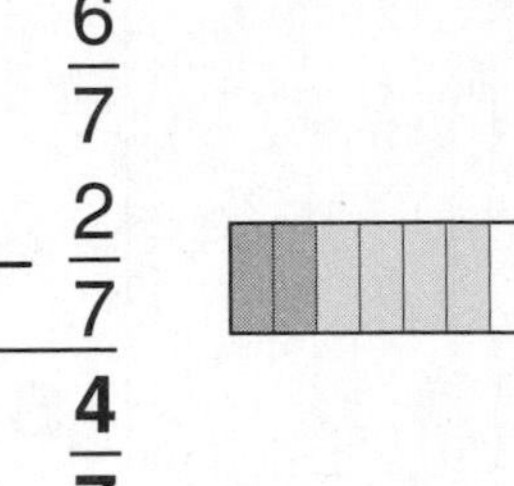

Example 2

The denominators are not the same.

$$\begin{array}{r} \frac{5}{6} \\ -\ \frac{1}{4} \\ \hline \end{array}$$

Rename each fraction with a common denominator.

Subtract the numerators.

$$\begin{array}{rcccc} & \frac{5}{6} & = \frac{5 * 2}{6 * 2} & = & \frac{10}{12} \\ - & \frac{1}{4} & = \frac{1 * 3}{4 * 3} & = & \frac{3}{12} \\ \hline & & & & \frac{7}{12} \end{array}$$

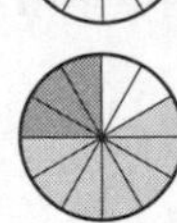

Subtraction

Check Your Understanding

Solve the following problems.

1. $\frac{4}{5} - \frac{2}{5}$ **2.** $\frac{7}{8} - \frac{3}{8}$ **3.** $\frac{7}{9} - \frac{5}{9}$ **4.** $\frac{2}{3} - \frac{1}{4}$

5. $\frac{1}{2} - \frac{3}{8}$ **6.** $\frac{3}{5} - \frac{1}{10}$ **7.** $\frac{7}{8} - \frac{5}{6}$ **8.** $\frac{11}{16} - \frac{2}{3}$

Write your answers on a separate sheet of paper.

Mixed-Number Subtraction

A mixed number names one or more wholes and a fractional part of a whole. For example, the mixed number $5\frac{1}{2}$ names 5 wholes and $\frac{1}{2}$ of another whole. Therefore, when problem solvers subtract mixed numbers, they combine the process of subtracting whole numbers and the process of subtracting fractions.

When subtracting mixed numbers, most people prefer to subtract the fractions first because this makes the process a bit less cumbersome when renaming is required. However, problem solvers with good number sense may approach such problems in either way.

Build Understanding

Ask students to draw a picture that shows $2\frac{1}{3}$. On the board, draw the picture on the right and write the fractions below it. Explain that $2\frac{1}{3}$ can be written as $1 + \frac{3}{3} + \frac{1}{3}$, or $1\frac{4}{3}$. Then have students rename $3\frac{1}{5}$ as $2 + \frac{5}{5} + \frac{1}{5} = 2\frac{6}{5}$ and $1\frac{1}{4}$ as $\frac{4}{4} + \frac{1}{4} = \frac{5}{4}$. Give students problems to try on their own.

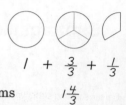

$1 + \frac{3}{3} + \frac{1}{3}$

$1\frac{4}{3}$

Using page 41, explain that when subtracting mixed numbers, students will need to rename the minuend (the top number) if the minuend is a whole number or if the fraction part of the minuend is smaller than the fraction part of the subtrahend. In Example 1, students must rename the whole number. Example 2 requires students first to rename the fractions so that they have a common denominator and then rename the minuend so that subtraction is possible. Use questions like the following to guide students through the examples:

- In Example 1, how is the minuend (5) renamed? *(as $4\frac{3}{3}$, so that it has the same denominator as the subtrahend $2\frac{2}{3}$)*
- In Example 2, what is the common denominator of $\frac{1}{3}$ and $\frac{1}{2}$? *(6)*
- In Example 2, why do you need to rename the minuend ($7\frac{2}{6}$) again? *(because $\frac{2}{6}$ in the minuend is smaller than $\frac{3}{6}$ in the subtrahend)*
- How do you rename $7\frac{2}{6}$? *(You rename it as $6 + \frac{6}{6} + \frac{2}{6}$, or $6\frac{8}{6}$.)*
- In Examples 1 and 2, do you need to simplify the difference? *(No. The difference is already in simplest form.)*

Error Alert Watch for students who rename a minuend like $2\frac{1}{5}$ as $2\frac{6}{5}$ instead of $1\frac{6}{5}$. Remind students that they are renaming 2 as $1\frac{5}{5}$. Crossing out the 2 and writing a 1 above it, similar to the way students regroup to subtract whole numbers, might be helpful. Also, make sure students simplify the difference if necessary after they are done subtracting.

Check Understanding

Write $7 - 4\frac{1}{5}$ on the board. Have a volunteer go to the board and solve the problem. Repeat the process with the following problems: $7\frac{2}{5} - 4\frac{1}{5}$, $7\frac{1}{5} - 4\frac{2}{5}$, and $7\frac{1}{5} - 4\frac{1}{3}$. Continue until you are reasonably certain that most of your students understand the algorithms. Then assign the "Check Your Understanding" exercises at the bottom of page 41. *(See answers in margin.)*

Page 41 Answer Key

1. $2\frac{3}{8}$
2. $\frac{2}{5}$
3. $2\frac{4}{7}$
4. $1\frac{1}{4}$
5. $\frac{5}{8}$
6. $3\frac{1}{2}$
7. $\frac{5}{12}$
8. $1\frac{7}{24}$

Name Date Time

Mixed-Number Subtraction

Use what you know about subtracting whole numbers and fractions to subtract mixed numbers. Check for like denominators when you subtract the fractions. Simplify the difference if necessary.

Example 1

$5 - 2\frac{2}{3}$

Rename the whole number. $4\frac{3}{3}$

Subtract the whole numbers. $-\ 2\frac{2}{3}$

Subtract the fractions.
Simplify the difference if necessary. $\mathbf{2\frac{1}{3}}$

Example 2

$7\frac{1}{3} - 5\frac{1}{2}$

Rename the fractions so that they have a common denominator. $7\frac{2}{6}$

Rename the minuend so that you can subtract. $-\ 5\frac{3}{6}$

Subtract the fractions. $6\frac{8}{6}$

Subtract the whole numbers.
Simplify the difference if necessary. $-\ 5\frac{3}{6}$

$\mathbf{1\frac{5}{6}}$

Check Your Understanding

Solve the following problems.

1. $4 - 1\frac{5}{8}$ **2.** $1 - \frac{3}{5}$ **3.** $3\frac{5}{7} - 1\frac{1}{7}$ **4.** $10\frac{1}{2} - 9\frac{1}{4}$

5. $2\frac{3}{8} - 1\frac{3}{4}$ **6.** $6\frac{1}{3} - 2\frac{5}{6}$ **7.** $1\frac{1}{12} - 1\frac{2}{3}$ **8.** $8\frac{1}{6} - 6\frac{7}{8}$

Subtraction

Write your answers on a separate sheet of paper.

FOCUS ALGORITHM

Partial-Products Multiplication

Page 43 Answer Key

1. 2,052
2. 3,612
3. 5,886
4. 3,965
5. 4,109
6. 1,392
7. 7,728
8. 42,635

Page 44 Answer Key

1. 3,510
2. 4,984
3. 6,164
4. 4,200
5. 2,832
6. 7,917
7. 6,080
8. 32,977

Page 45 Answer Key

1. 8,464
2. 33,824
3. 20,454
4. 55,878
5. 72,075
6. 18,915
7. 43,395
8. 205,771

Partial-products multiplication is based on the distributive, or grouping, property of multiplication. A person using this algorithm multiplies each digit of one factor by each of the digits in the other factor, taking into account the place value of each digit. Then the person adds all the partial products to find the total product (each partial product is either a multiplication fact or an extended multiplication fact.)

Students find this algorithm particularly useful for estimating the magnitude of a total product.

Build Understanding

Conduct a quick, oral review of multiples of 10, 100, and 1,000. Call out problems and have the class answer in unison. Begin with simple multiples, such as "2 [10s]," "3 [100s]," and "5 [1,000s]." Avoid saying "2 times 10" because saying (and thinking) "2 tens" emphasizes place value. After a bit of practice, move on to larger multiples of 10, 100, and 1,000, such as 60 [80s], 9 [3,000s], and 40 [500s].

Finally, emphasize the patterns in successive multiples of 10. Have a student come to the board and write the answers to 7 [10s], 7 [100s], 7 [1,000s], and 7 [10,000s]. Ask students to explain the pattern they see emerging. Guide them to conclude that each successive product has one more zero than the product before it.

Using page 43, explain that with this method of multiplying, students can find the partial products in any order. However, starting with the greatest place-value digit in each factor—the one on the far-left side of each factor—will help them keep track of the place values better. Use questions like the following to guide students through each example:

- Which two digits are multiplied to get the first partial product?
- Which partial product is the result of multiplying the two ones digits? *(the last partial product)*
- Can you tell right away how many partial products a problem will have? *(Yes. Observing how many times each digit in one factor must be multiplied by each of the digits in the other factor tells you how many partial products there will be.)*

Error Alert Be sure students know the correct place value of each digit in each factor. For instance, in Example 1 you might notice students multiplying 9×4 instead of 9×40. If it helps students, ask them to draw vertical lines to separate the place-value columns and have them write place-value abbreviations (100s, 10s, and 1s) above the columns.

Check Understanding

Write $637 * 18$ on the board and solve it using the partial-products algorithm. Then have a volunteer or two come to the board, point to each pair of digits that were multiplied to produce each partial product, and explain the value of each of those digits. Do as many examples in this way as necessary, until you are reasonably certain that most of your students understand the algorithm. Then assign the "Check Your Understanding" exercises at the bottom of page 43. For practice of more difficult problems, refer to pages 44 and 45. *(See answers in margin.)*

Name Date Time

Partial-Products Multiplication

FOCUS ALGORITHM

Multiply each digit in the bottom factor by each digit in the top factor. Then add all of the partial products to find the total product.

Example 1

			100s	10s	1s	
			2	4	5	(factor)
		×			9	(factor)
Multiply 9 × 200.	→	1	8	0	0	
Multiply 9 × 40.	→		3	6	0	
Multiply 9 × 5.	→	+		4	5	
Add the partial products.	→	**2,**	**2**	**0**	**5**	(product)

Example 2

			100s	10s	1s	
			7	4	2	(factor)
		×			5	(factor)
Multiply 5 × 700.	→	3	5	0	0	
Multiply 5 × 40.	→		2	0	0	
Multiply 5 × 2.	→	+		1	0	
Add the partial products.	→	**3,**	**7**	**1**	**0**	(product)

Multiplication

Check Your Understanding

Solve the following problems.

1. 342 × 6 **2.** 903 × 4 **3.** 654 × 9

4. 793 × 5 **5.** 587 × 7 **6.** 464 × 3

7. 966 × 8 **8.** 8,527 × 5

Write your answers on a separate sheet of paper.

Name Date Time

FOCUS ALGORITHM

Partial-Products Multiplication

Multiply each digit in the bottom factor by each digit in the top factor. Then add all of the partial products to find the total product.

Example 1

			10s	1s	
			5	6	(factor)
	×		8	2	(factor)
Multiply 80 × 50. →	4	0	0	0	
Multiply 80 × 6. →		4	8	0	
Multiply 2 × 50. →		1	0	0	
Multiply 2 × 6. →	+		1	2	
Add the partial products. →	**4,**	**5**	**9**	**2**	(product)

Example 2

			10s	1s	
			9	4	(factor)
	×		7	6	(factor)
Multiply 70 × 90. →	6	3	0	0	
Multiply 70 × 4. →		2	8	0	
Multiply 6 × 90. →		5	4	0	
Multiply 6 × 4. →	+		2	4	
Add the partial products. →	**7,**	**1**	**4**	**4**	(product)

Multiplication

Check Your Understanding

Solve the following problems.

1. 45 × 78 **2.** 89 × 56 **3.** 67 × 92

4. 56 × 75 **5.** 59 × 48 **6.** 91 × 87

7. 64 × 95 **8.** 673 × 49

Write your answers on a separate sheet of paper.

Name Date Time

Partial-Products Multiplication

FOCUS ALGORITHM

Multiply each digit in the bottom factor by each digit in the top factor. Then add all of the partial products to find the total product.

Example Show Me

		100s	10s	1s	
			7	5	2 (factor)
	*			4	6 (factor)
Multiply 40 * 700. →	2	8	0	0	0
Multiply 40 * 50. →		2	0	0	0
Multiply 40 * 2. →				8	0
Multiply 6 * 700. →		4	2	0	0
Multiply 6 * 50. →			3	0	0
Multiply 6 * 2. →	+			1	2
Add the partial products. →	**3**	**4,**	**5**	**9**	**2** (product)

Multiplication

Check Your Understanding

Solve the following problems.

1. 368 * 23 **2.** 604 * 56 **3.** 974 * 21

4. 834 * 67 **5.** 775 * 93 **6.** 485 * 39

7. 789 * 55 **8.** 593 * 347

Write your answers on a separate sheet of paper.

U.S. Traditional Multiplication (Standard) with Models

U.S. traditional multiplication (standard) is familiar to most adults and many children. A person using this algorithm multiplies from right to left, regrouping as necessary.

The traditional method for teaching this algorithm is to begin with models (such as base-10 blocks), using them to demonstrate the regrouping process.

Build Understanding

Divide the class into small groups and distribute base-10 blocks to each group. Ask each group to use the least number of blocks to represent the number 26. (They should show 2 tens and 6 ones.) Then write the problem 26 × 2 on the board, and ask the groups to model the problem, using the least number of blocks to show the product. Check to see how many students traded 10 ones for 1 ten, which would give them a total of 5 tens and 2 ones.

Using page 47, explain that with this method of multiplying, students will begin multiplying the ones digits. Use questions like the following to guide students through the example:

- Why does the first step of the model have 3 sets of blocks with 2 tens and 7 ones in each? *(because the top factor, 27, has 2 tens and 7 ones, —and we're multiplying those 2 tens and 7 ones 3 times)*
- Why are the 21 ones grouped together in the first step of the model? *(to show that we multiply the ones digits first)*
- In the second step of the model, why have the 21 ones been replaced by 2 tens and 1 one? *(to show the renaming, or regrouping, that is taking place)*

Error Alert Watch for students who misalign the products under the factors. If it helps students, allow them to draw vertical lines between the place-value columns, and show them how to extend the lines below the problem so that the lines will help guide them as they record the answer.

Check Understanding

Divide the class into pairs, designating a "writer" and a "solver" within each partnership. Give partners problems to solve together. The "solver" should dictate the solution to the "writer." You might use any of the following problems (and add some of your own as needed): 13 ∗ 4; 85 ∗ 2; 61 ∗ 7; 11 ∗ 5; 22 ∗ 3; 49 ∗ 6. Explain that the "writer" should challenge the "solver" whenever the "writer" thinks a direction is incorrect. Then have partners switch tasks and work through a second problem. When you are reasonably certain that most of your students understand the algorithm, assign the "Check Your Understanding" exercises at the bottom of page 47. *(See answers in margin.)*

Page 47 Answer Key

1. 192

2. 448

3. 485

4. 1,515

5. 1,164

6. 6,713

7. 3,264

8. 1,485

Name Date Time

U.S. Traditional Multiplication (Standard)

Use blocks to model the problem. Multiply from right to left. Then find the total.

Example

Multiply the ones.
(3 × 7 = 21 ones)

$$\begin{array}{r} 27 \\ \times\ \ 3 \\ \hline \end{array}$$

Rename 21 ones as 2 tens and 1 one.

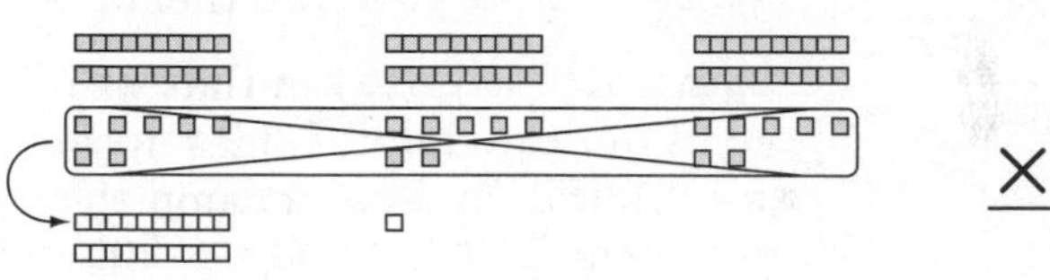

$$\begin{array}{r} {}^{2} \\ 27 \\ \times\ \ 3 \\ \hline 1 \end{array}$$

Multiply the tens.
(3 × 2 tens = 6 tens)

$$\begin{array}{r} {}^{2} \\ 27 \\ \times\ \ 3 \\ \hline 1 \end{array}$$

Add the remaining tens.
(6 tens + 2 tens = 8 tens)

$$\begin{array}{r} {}^{2} \\ 27 \\ \times\ \ 3 \\ \hline 81 \end{array}$$

The product of **3** and **27** is **81**.

Check Your Understanding

Solve the following problems.

1. 64 × 3 **2.** 56 ∗ 8 **3.** 97 × 5

4. 505 ∗ 3 **5.** 291 ∗ 4 **6.** 137 × 49

7. 816 ∗ 4 **8.** 495 ∗ 3

Write your answers on a separate sheet of paper.

U.S. Traditional Multiplication (Standard)

U.S. traditional multiplication (standard) is familiar to most adults and many children. A person using this algorithm multiplies from right to left, regrouping as necessary.

The traditional method for teaching this algorithm is to begin with models (such as base-10 blocks) and then gradually move toward the use of symbols (that is, numerals) only.

Build Understanding

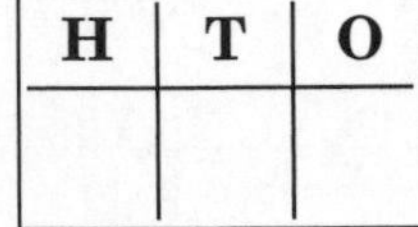

H	T	O

Since students will need a sharp eye for place value to succeed with this algorithm, conduct a basic-facts review—with a place-value twist. Have students take out their slates and chalk, or paper and pencils. On their slates, have them copy the chart shown in the margin. Tell them that you will call out problems and that they should write the answers on their slates with the digits written correctly in the chart.

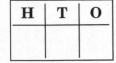

Ask a volunteer to read her or his answer and identify the value of each digit (for example: "72; 7 tens and 2 ones"). After reviewing some of the basic multiplication facts, expand the review to include multiples of ten. Use such problems as 30 * 8; 60 * 4; 200 * 7; and 500 * 5. Make sure students expand their place-value charts to accommodate their 3- and 4-digit answers.

Using page 49, explain that with this method of multiplying, students will begin with the ones digit in the bottom factor. Use questions such as the following to guide students through the example (and through other examples you provide):

- Will you begin multiplying with the digits on the right or on the left? *(on the right)*
- What is the correct method for recording each individual product? *(If the product has one digit, align it in the correct column under the two factors. If the product has two digits, align the right digit below the two factors, in the correct column, and regroup the left digit at the top of the next place-value column to the left. If there are no columns to the left, then record the 2-digit answer.)*

Error Alert Watch for students who skip a digit when they multiply a 3-digit number by a 2-digit number. Have students use their index fingers to point to each digit in the top factor as they work. This method may help ensure that students multiply every digit in the bottom factor by every digit in the top factor.

Check Understanding

Divide students into pairs. Have them solve the problem 572 * 43. Tell them to write neatly, and then have them exchange papers with their partners. Direct students to check each other's problems. If they find a mistake, ask them to identify the mistake. When you are reasonably certain that most of your students understand the algorithm, assign the "Check Your Understanding" exercises at the bottom of page 49. *(See answers in margin.)*

Page 49 Answer Key

1. 432

2. 210

3. 558

4. 11,051

5. 7,975

6. 36,064

7. 19,203

8. 57,908

Name Date Time

U.S. Traditional Multiplication (Standard)

First, multiply the ones digit in the bottom factor by the ones digit in the top factor. Record any regrouping at the top of the next place-value column. Then, multiply each of the remaining digits in the bottom factor by each of the remaining digits in the top factor, moving from right to left. Finally, if you have partial products, add them to find the total product.

Example 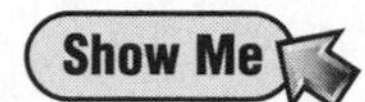

Multiply 5 ones by 4 ones. *(20 ones)*
Rename 20 ones as 2 tens and 0 ones.
Record the 0 ones in the ones column.
Record the 2 tens at the top of the tens column.

→

$$\begin{array}{r} {\scriptstyle 2} \\ 34 \\ * \ 15 \\ \hline 0 \end{array}$$

Multiply 5 ones by 3 tens. *(15 tens)*
Add 2 tens. *(15 tens + 2 tens = 17 tens)*
Record the 17 tens.

→

$$\begin{array}{r} {\scriptstyle 2} \\ 34 \\ * \ 15 \\ \hline 170 \end{array}$$

Multiply 1 ten by 4 ones *(40)* and 1 ten by 3 tens *(300)*.
Record 340.

→

Add the partial products to find the final product.

$$\begin{array}{r} {\scriptstyle 2} \\ 34 \\ * \ \ 15 \\ \hline 170 \\ +\ 340 \\ \hline 510 \end{array}$$

Multiplication

Check Your Understanding

Solve the following problems.

1. 54 * 8 **2.** 70 × 3 **3.** 62 * 9 **4.** 257 * 43

5. 319 × 25 **6.** 784 * 46 **7.** 519 × 37 **8.** 467 * 124

FOCUS ALGORITHM

Partial-Products Multiplication for Decimals

Partial-products multiplication can be applied to decimal multiplication. The only difference is that the decimal place value will be ignored until the end solution is recorded. Students find this algorithm particularly helpful for estimating the location of the decimal point. The challenge is to understand where to correctly position the decimal point in the product, a process that requires greater number sense and estimation skills than required in whole number multiplication.

Methods that improve students' understanding of decimal multiplication include using models (base-10 blocks) to show repeated addition or groupings, using calculators to look for patterns in the decimals, and rounding factors to find a reasonable estimate, or magnitude estimate, for the product.

Build Understanding

If students need to review the whole-number version of this algorithm, refer them to pages 43–45.

Review the process of making a magnitude estimate of the product in a decimal multiplication problem. Write the problem 3.8 * 4.3 on the board. Explain that each of these numbers can be rounded to 4. Since 4 * 4 = 16, the product will be in the tens. Have students practice finding magnitude estimates for problems like this on their own. Provide opportunities to share strategies.

Using page 51, explain that students should first make a magnitude estimate for the answer. Then they should multiply just as they would with the whole-number version of the partial-products algorithm. Finally, they should use their magnitude estimate to help them place the decimal point in the answer. Use questions like the following to guide students through each example:

- Which two digits are multiplied to get the first partial product?
- How can you tell how many partial products you will end up with? *(Observing how many times each digit in one factor must be multiplied by each digit in the other factor tells how many partial products there will be.)*
- What is a reasonable estimate for the answer of this problem?
- Based on the estimate, where will you place the decimal point?

Error Alert Be sure students remember to ignore the decimal points as they work the problem using the partial-products algorithm for whole numbers. Once the total for the partial product is recorded, check to see that students use their magnitude estimate to help them place the decimal point correctly in the answer. If needed, require students to record their magnitude estimate so you can check their understanding.

Check Understanding

Write 4.5 * 32 on the board and solve it using the partial-products algorithm, ignoring the decimal point. Then have a volunteer or two come to the board and point to each pair of digits that were multiplied to produce each partial product. Have students also explain how they would use a magnitude estimate for the product to help them decide where to place the decimal point. Repeat the process until you are reasonably certain that most of your students understand the algorithm. Then assign the "Check Your Understanding" exercises at the bottom of page 51. *(See answers in margin.)*

Page 51 Answer Key

1. 29.88

2. 33.32

3. 24.284

4. 62.175

5. 33.12

6. 19.72

7. 53.82

8. 48.0501

Name Date Time

Partial-Products Multiplication for Decimals

FOCUS ALGORITHM

First, make a magnitude estimate. Next, multiply each digit in the bottom factor by each digit in the top factor. Then add all of the partial products. Use your magnitude estimate to correctly place the decimal point in the product.

Example

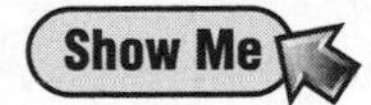

Step 1: Make a magnitude estimate. 7.4 * 6.9

Round 7.4 to 7 and 6.9 to 7.
Since 7 * 7 = 49, the product will be in the tens.

Step 2: Multiply as you would for whole numbers.

		74	(factor)
		* 69	(factor)
Multiply 60 * 70.	→	4200	
Multiply 60 * 4.	→	240	
Multiply 9 * 70.	→	630	
Multiply 9 * 4.	→	+ 36	
Add the partial products.	→	5106	

Step 3: Place the decimal point correctly in the answer. Since the magnitude estimate is in the tens, the product must be in the tens.

7.4 * 6.9 = 51.06 (product)

Multiplication

Check Your Understanding

Solve the following problems.

1. 8.3 * 3.6 **2.** 6.8 * 4.9 **3.** 5.2 * 4.67 **4.** 8.29 * 7.5

5. 7.2 * 4.6 **6.** 5.8 * 3.4 **7.** 6.9 * 7.8 **8.** 6.09 * 7.89

Write your answers on a separate sheet of paper.

Lattice Multiplication

Lattice multiplication has been traced to India, where it was in use before A.D. 1100. It derives its name from the lattice within which the person using the algorithm writes each partial product (see facing page). The problem solver finds the final product by adding all the numerals along each of the diagonals within the lattice.

Many Everyday Mathematics® *students find this particular multiplication algorithm to be one of their favorites. It helps them keep track of all the partial products without having to write extra zeros—and it helps them practice their multiplication facts.*

Build Understanding

Introduce the lattice algorithm for multiplication by saying that this is a multiplication method in which the numbers are placed around and within a lattice—a special kind of grid in which the dotted-line "rails" within the cells help form diagonals. Invite students to speculate about why a lattice might be a good way to organize a multiplication problem. Help students realize that a lattice can help the problem solver keep track of the many digits that result from the multiplication of two multidigit factors.

Using page 53, explain that with this method of multiplying, students will be multiplying one digit of each factor by one digit of the other factor and recording each partial product within a cell in the grid. Use questions like the following to guide students through the example (and through other examples you provide):

- Which two numbers are being multiplied? *(The numbers written along the top of the lattice and the outer right side of the lattice. In the example, the two numbers being multiplied are 26 and 35.)*
- Which two-digit number is written in the upper right-hand cell? *(The number that is the product of the two digits along both sides of the right-hand corner of the lattice. In the example, the two-digit number in the upper right-hand cell is 18—the product of 3 and 6.)*
- Where do you start when adding the numbers inside the lattice? *(You begin with the bottom right-hand corner and add along each diagonal, moving toward the upper left-hand corner.)*

Error Alert Be sure that students enter 0 in the top half of a cell when the product is less than 10. (See the digits written in the top left-hand corner of the lattice.) And, as students add the numbers within each diagonal, be certain that they are regrouping correctly: They must regroup each tens digit up to the top of the next diagonal.

Check Understanding

Have a few volunteers demonstrate this algorithm on the board. Guide their descriptions when necessary and demonstrate a couple of extra problems yourself. When you are reasonably certain that most of your students understand the algorithm, assign the "Check Your Understanding" exercises at the bottom of page 53. *(See answers in margin.)*

Page 53 Answer Key

1. 308

2. 792

3. 2,340

4. 3,362

5. 3,796

6. 2,688

7. 17,595

8. 488,592

Name Date Time

Lattice Multiplication

Write one factor along the top of the grid. Write the other factor along the right side of the grid. Begin with the first digit from the side factor, and multiply each digit in the top factor by each digit in the side factor. Record each answer in its own cell, placing the tens digit in the upper half of the cell and the ones digit in the bottom half of the cell. Then add along each diagonal and record any regroupings as shown below.

Example

Multiply 3 × 6. **Record** the product in the upper right-hand cell.

Multiply 3 × 2. **Record** the product in the upper left-hand cell.

Multiply 5 × 6. **Record** the product in the lower right-hand cell.

Multiply 5 × 2. **Record** the product in the lower left-hand cell.

Add along each diagonal beginning with the bottom right diagonal. Work toward the upper left diagonal. **Regroup** each tens digit to the top of the next diagonal (to help you remember to add that digit).

The product of **26** and **35** is **910.**

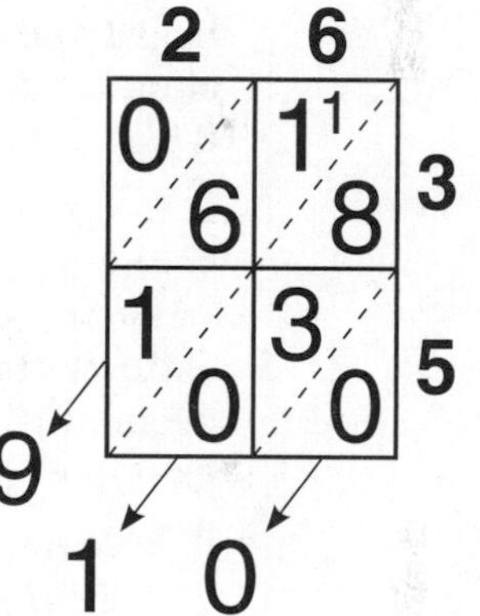

Multiplication

Check Your Understanding

Solve the following problems.

1. 14 × 22 **2.** 44 ∗ 18 **3.** 65 ∗ 36

4. 82 ∗ 41 **5.** 73 × 52 **6.** 96 ∗ 28

7. 391 ∗ 45 **8.** 624 × 783

Write your answers on a separate sheet of paper.

U.S. Traditional Multiplication for Decimals (Standard)

U.S. traditional multiplication for decimals (standard) is familiar to most adults and many children. The algorithm is applied to decimals just as one would apply it to whole numbers, with the additional challenge of understanding where to place the decimal point in the product. To be successful, students must apply their number sense and their estimation skills.

Methods that improve students' understanding of decimal multiplication include using models (base-10 blocks) to show repeated addition or groupings, using calculators to look for patterns in the decimals, and rounding factors to find a reasonable range for the product.

Build Understanding

If students need to review the whole-number version of this algorithm, refer them to page 49.

Review the process of estimating products of decimals. Write 2.8 * 1.3 on the board and ask students to estimate the answer. Guide students to see that since 2.8 is almost 3, and 1.3 is between 1 and 2, the answer will be between 3 (3 * 1) and 6 (3 * 2). Then have students find the range for the problem 30.8 * 4.7.

Using page 54, explain that with this method of decimal multiplication, students will multiply the factors as if they were whole numbers and then estimate to find a range for the answer, using their number sense to place the decimal point. Use questions like the following to guide students through the example:

- What do you need to do first? *(Rewrite the problem using whole numbers. In the example, 4.8 * 7.3 should be written as 48 * 73.)*
- Why must 4.8 * 7.3 be greater than 28 (4 * 7)? *(4.8 is greater than 4, and 7.3 is greater than 7, so 4.8 * 7.3 is greater than 4 * 7.)*
- Why must 4.8 * 7.3 be less than 40 (5 * 8)? *(4.8 is less than 5, and 7.3 is less than 8, so 4.8 * 7.3 is less than 5 * 8.)*
- Where do you place the decimal point in 3504 so that the product is between 28 and 40? *(between the 5 and the 0: 35.04)*
- What is a "shortcut" method to use when figuring out where to place the decimal point? *(Count the total number of decimal places in both factors. It should be the same as the number of decimal places in the product.)*

Error Alert Watch for students who incorrectly place the decimal point. Remind students that they can always simply count the total number of decimal places in both factors to determine how many decimal places should be in the product.

Check Understanding

Have a student make up a problem that he or she considers easy and write it on the board. Then have a volunteer go to the board and solve the problem. Repeat the process until you are reasonably certain that most of your students understand the algorithm. Then assign the "Check Your Understanding" exercises at the bottom of page 55. *(See answers in margin.)*

Page 55 Answer Key

1. 9.25

2. 51.84

3. 25.74

4. 54.29

5. 187

6. 1,476.3

7. 2,851.2

8. 13.448

Name Date Time

U.S. Traditional Multiplication for Decimals (Standard)

Use what you already know about multiplying whole numbers using U.S. traditional multiplication. Round the factors and multiply mentally to find a sensible range for the product. Use this sensible range to help you correctly place the decimal point in the product.

Example

4.8 ∗ 7.3

Multiply as you would with whole numbers.

Estimate to place the decimal point in the answer.

- 4.8 is between 4 and 5.
- 7.3 is between 7 and 8.
- The product of 4.8 and 7.3 is between 28 (4 ∗ 7) and 40 (5 ∗ 8).
- 35.04 is between 28 and 40.

```
    2
   48
 * 73
 ----
  144
+3360
 ----
 3504
```

or

Count the total number of decimal places in both factors to place the decimal point in the answer. (The total number of decimal places in both factors will equal the number of decimal places in the product.)

4.8 ∗ 7.3 = 35.04

Multiplication

Check Your Understanding

Solve the following problems.

1. 3.7 ∗ 2.5 **2.** 8.1 × 6.4 **3.** 3.3 × 7.8

4. 6.1 ∗ 8.9 **5.** 34 × 5.5 **6.** 70.3 ∗ 21

7. 891 × 3.2 **8.** 6.56 ∗ 2.05

Write your answers on a separate sheet of paper.

Lattice Multiplication for Decimals

Lattice multiplication, a favorite of many Everyday Mathematics® *students, can be adapted and applied to decimal multiplication. The challenge is to understand where to correctly position the decimal point in the product, a process that requires greater number sense and estimation skills than required in decimal addition and subtraction.*

Provide opportunities for students to explore decimal multiplication before trying to apply familiar multiplication algorithms. Methods that improve students' understanding of decimal multiplication include using models to show repeated addition or groupings, using calculators to look for patterns, and rounding factors to find a reasonable range for the product.

Build Understanding

If students need to review the whole-number version of this algorithm, refer them to page 53.

Review the process of finding a reasonable range for the answer to a multiplication problem. Explain that the answer to 2.8 * 3.2 is going to be greater than 6 (2 × 3) because 2.8 is greater than 2 and 3.2 is greater than 3. The answer to 2.8 * 3.2 is going to be less than 12 (3 × 4) because 2.8 is less than 3 and 3.2 is less than 4. So, 2.8 * 3.2 is going to be between 6 and 12. Have students practice finding ranges for a few problems like this on their own.

Using page 57, explain that students multiply just as they do with the whole-number version of the lattice multiplication. Then, they find a reasonable range for the answer and use the range to place the decimal point. Use questions like the following to guide students through the example:

- Which two numbers are being multiplied? *(The numbers written along the outside top of the lattice and the outer right side of the lattice.)*
- Which two-digit number goes in the lower left-hand cell? *(The product of the upper left-hand digit and the lower right-hand digit. In the example, the two-digit number in the lower-left hand cell is 06—the product of 1 and 6.)*
- Why do you need to find a reasonable range for the answer? *(to know where to place the decimal point)*
- How do you find a reasonable range for the answer? *(You round both of the numbers down and multiply to get a low estimate; then you round both of the numbers up and multiply to get a high estimate. The range is between the low estimate and the high estimate.)*

Error Alert Be sure students enter 0 in the top half of a cell when the product is less than 10. Watch for students who do not add correctly along each diagonal: They must regroup each tens digit up to the top of the next diagonal.

Check Understanding

Have a volunteer go to the board and use lattice multiplication to solve 1.4 * 6.2. Encourage the student to explain what he or she is doing while working so that the class can follow along. Have students direct their questions to the volunteer, and guide that student in answering as necessary. When you are reasonably certain that most of your students understand the algorithm, assign the "Check Your Understanding" exercises at the bottom of page 57. *(Answers in margin.)*

Page 57 Answer Key

1. 11.61

2. 5.58

3. 49.4

4. 31.62

5. 91.3

6. 403.2

7. 62.7

8. 9.702

Name Date Time

Lattice Multiplication for Decimals

Use what you already know about multiplying whole numbers using lattice multiplication. To correctly place the decimal point in the product, estimate the product. You can also use the method explained below for placing the decimal point.

Example 

6.5 ∗ 3.1

Multiply as you would with whole numbers.

Multiply 3 ∗ 5. Record the product in the upper right-hand cell.

Multiply 3 ∗ 6. Record the product in the upper left-hand cell.

Multiply 1 ∗ 5. Record the product in the lower right-hand cell.

Multiply 1 ∗ 6. Record the product in the lower left-hand cell.

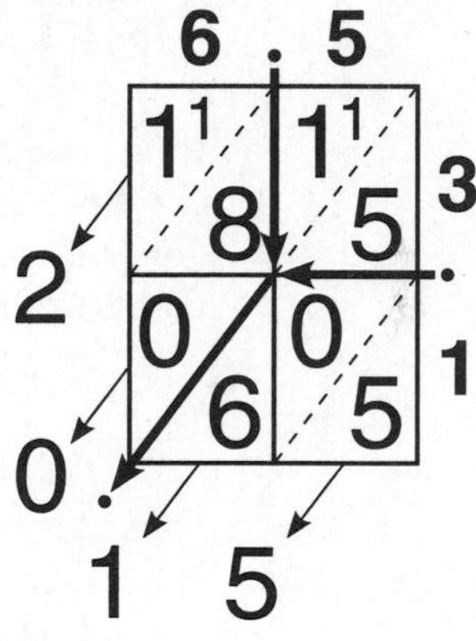

Add along each diagonal, starting at the bottom right. **Regroup** as necessary.

To place the decimal point, find the intersection of the decimal points along the horizontal and vertical lines; then slide it down along the diagonal.

6.5 ∗ 3.1 = 20.15

Multiplication

Check Your Understanding

Solve the following problems.

1. 2.7 ∗ 4.3 **2.** 3.1 × 1.8 **3.** 7.6 × 6.5

4. 9.3 ∗ 3.4 **5.** 83 × 1.1 **6.** 5.6 ∗ 72

7. 11 × 5.7 **8.** 9.9 ∗ 0.98

Write your answers on a separate sheet of paper.

Fraction Multiplication

When the factors are easy to work with, an area model is a good way to find the product of two fractions. This method is useful as a first multiplication method for students because it helps them visualize the multiplication process. It also helps students relate the values of the denominators of the factors to the value of the denominator of the product.

Once students have experience with the area model and an understanding of fraction multiplication, they are ready to apply the Multiplication of Fractions Property. When doing so, problem solvers multiply the numerators of the factors and multiply the denominators of the factors to name the numerator and denominator in the product.

Build Understanding

Using page 59, show students the area model for multiplying fractions. The area model is a good representation of what it means to multiply two fractions. The first diagram in Example 1 shows one fraction, $\frac{3}{4}$, and the second diagram shows $\frac{1}{3}$ of $\frac{3}{4}$. Spend time with the area model before moving on to the algorithm that uses the Multiplication of Fractions Property (Example 2).

Use questions like the following to guide students through the examples:

- How do you find $\frac{3}{4}$ of a region? *(You divide a region into 4 equal parts and shade 3 of them.)*
- How do you find $\frac{1}{3}$ of a region? *(You divide a region into 3 equal parts and shade 1 part.)*
- What part of the diagram shows $\frac{1}{3} * \frac{3}{4}$? *(the region where the shading overlaps)*
- In Example 2, which numbers do you multiply to find the product of the two fractions? *(You multiply one numerator by the other numerator. You multiply one denominator by the other denominator.)*

Error Alert Watch for students who incorrectly identify the product on an area model. Different-color markers might help students see the overlap clearly. Make sure students using the Multiplication of Fractions Property multiply both the numerators and the denominators.

Check Understanding

Divide the class into groups of 2. Give students this problem to solve: $\frac{1}{4} * \frac{2}{3}$. Have one partner draw an area model to solve the problem. Have the other partner use the Multiplication of Fractions Property to solve the problem. The partners then compare the answers to make sure they are the same. If they are not the same, they correct their work. Then have partners switch roles to solve this problem: $\frac{2}{5} * \frac{1}{2}$. Circulate around the room checking students' work. When you are reasonably certain that most of your students understand the area model and Multiplication of Fractions Property, assign the "Check Your Understanding" exercises at the bottom of page 59. *(See answers in margin.)*

Page 59 Answer Key

1. $\frac{1}{4}$
2. $\frac{7}{20}$
3. $\frac{3}{10}$
4. $\frac{2}{7}$
5. $\frac{1}{3}$
6. $\frac{10}{27}$
7. $\frac{6}{35}$
8. $\frac{1}{8}$

Name Date Time

Fraction Multiplication

An area model and the Multiplication of Fractions Property are two methods you can use to multiply fractions.

Example 1 **Area Model** $\frac{1}{3} * \frac{3}{4}$

Show $\frac{3}{4}$ of a region shaded.

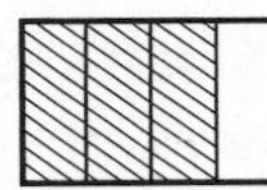

Show $\frac{1}{3}$ of that region shaded.

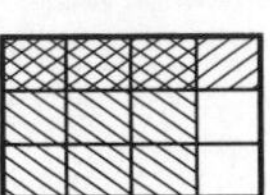

The portion that overlaps shows $\frac{1}{3}$ of $\frac{3}{4}$. $\mathbf{\frac{1}{3} * \frac{3}{4} = \frac{3}{12}}$, **or** $\mathbf{\frac{1}{4}}$

Example 2 **Multiplication of Fractions Property** $\frac{5}{6} * \frac{1}{2}$

Multiply the numerators.

Multiply the denominators.

$\mathbf{\frac{5}{6} * \frac{1}{2} = \frac{5 * 1}{6 * 2} = \frac{5}{12}}$

Multiplication

Check Your Understanding

Solve the following problems.

1. $\frac{3}{8} * \frac{2}{3}$ **2.** $\frac{1}{2} * \frac{7}{10}$ **3.** $\frac{2}{5} * \frac{3}{4}$ **4.** $\frac{1}{3} * \frac{6}{7}$

5. $\frac{5}{9} * \frac{3}{5}$ **6.** $\frac{5}{9} * \frac{2}{3}$ **7.** $\frac{3}{5} * \frac{4}{14}$ **8.** $\frac{3}{14} * \frac{7}{12}$

Write your answers on a separate sheet of paper.

Mixed-Number Multiplication

The algorithms people choose for multiplying mixed numbers depend on the values of the factors and how easy they are to work with. By renaming both factors as fractions, problem solvers can proceed directly with fraction multiplication. This method is surely accurate and is the one typically taught to students. However, when one of the factors is a whole number and the other a mixed number, it may be more efficient to apply the distributive property—multiplying each part of the mixed-number factor by the whole-number factor.

Build Understanding

Review the process of renaming a mixed number as a fraction. Write $3\frac{1}{3}$ on the board and explain how to rename this mixed number as a fraction ($\frac{10}{3}$). Then have students rename the following mixed numbers at their desks: $2\frac{1}{4}$; $3\frac{2}{3}$; $1\frac{1}{8}$. Ask volunteers to write the answers on the board.

Using page 61, explain that there are two ways to multiply mixed numbers. In Example 1, both factors are mixed numbers. Students first rename each number as a fraction and then use the Multiplication of Fractions Property to multiply the fractions. In Example 2, one of the factors is a whole number. Students could use the same method they use for multiplying mixed numbers, but the method shown in Example 2 often results in simpler computation. This method uses the distributive property: Students consider the mixed number as two parts, a whole number and a fraction, and each of these parts is multiplied by the whole number. Students then add the partial products. Use questions like the following to guide students through the examples:

- What is $2\frac{1}{2}$ renamed as a fraction? *($\frac{5}{2}$)*
- Why is $\frac{20}{6}$ equal to $3\frac{2}{6}$? *($20 \div 6 = 3$ R2. The whole-number part of the quotient is the whole-number part of the mixed number; the remainder is the numerator of the fraction in the mixed number; and the divisor is the denominator of the fraction in the mixed number.)*
- What two steps do you follow to multiply 5 by $3\frac{1}{4}$? *(5×3 and $5 \times \frac{1}{4}$)*

Error Alert Watch for students who have difficulty writing mixed numbers as fractions. Many students multiply the whole-number part of the mixed number by the denominator of the fraction part but forget to add the numerator of the fraction. For example, these students might rename $2\frac{1}{3}$ as $\frac{6}{3}$. Also, watch for students who multiply the partial products instead of adding them.

Check Understanding

Write $8 \times 3\frac{2}{7}$ on the board. Have two volunteers go to the board and work through this problem. Ask one volunteer to use the standard algorithm, and ask the other to use the algorithm shown in Example 2. Students should get the same result using the two algorithms, but they will notice that the computation using the second algorithm is simpler. When you are reasonably certain that most of your students understand both algorithms, assign the "Check Your Understanding" exercises at the bottom of page 61. *(See answers in margin.)*

Page 61 Answer Key

1. $1\frac{7}{8}$

2. $3\frac{4}{15}$

3. $4\frac{2}{9}$

4. 15

5. $25\frac{3}{5}$

6. 57

7. $5\frac{5}{16}$

8. $10\frac{13}{24}$

Name Date Time

Mixed-Number Multiplication

Here are two ways to multiply mixed numbers. The method you use usually depends on the values of the factors.

Example 1 Change-to-Fractions Algorithm (Standard)

$2\frac{1}{2} * 1\frac{1}{3}$

Rename the mixed numbers as fractions.

$\frac{5}{2} * \frac{4}{3}$

Multiply the fractions.

$\frac{5 * 4}{2 * 3} = \frac{20}{6}$

Rename the product as a mixed number. Simplify the product if necessary.

$\frac{20}{6} = 3\frac{2}{6} = 3\frac{1}{3}$

$\mathbf{2\frac{1}{2} * 1\frac{1}{3} = 3\frac{1}{3}}$

Example 2 Multiplying a Whole Number and a Mixed Number

$5 * 3\frac{1}{4}$

Multiply the whole number by each part of the mixed number.

$5 * (3 + \frac{1}{4})$

$(5 * 3) + (5 * \frac{1}{4})$

Add the partial products. Simplify the product if necessary.

$15 + \frac{5}{4} = 15\frac{5}{4}$

$15\frac{5}{4} = 16\frac{1}{4}$

$\mathbf{5 * 3\frac{1}{4} = 16\frac{1}{4}}$

Multiplication

Check Your Understanding

Solve the following problems.

1. $1\frac{1}{2} \times 1\frac{1}{4}$ **2.** $2\frac{1}{3} \times 1\frac{2}{5}$ **3.** $3\frac{1}{6} * 1\frac{1}{3}$ **4.** $6 * 2\frac{1}{2}$

5. $3\frac{1}{5} \times 8$ **6.** $12 \times 4\frac{3}{4}$ **7.** $2\frac{1}{8} * 2\frac{1}{2}$ **8.** $3\frac{5}{6} * 2\frac{3}{4}$

Write your answers on a separate sheet of paper.

FOCUS ALGORITHM

Partial-Quotients Division

In partial-quotients division, it takes several steps to find the quotient. At each step, you find a partial answer (called a **partial quotient***); then you find the product of the partial quotient and divisor and subtract it from the dividend. Finally, you add all the partial quotients to find the final quotient.*

Even those students whose basic-facts knowledge and estimation skills are limited can find correct answers using this commonsense approach. In the process, students quickly discover that the better their estimates, the fewer the steps.

Build Understanding

Using page 63, explain that with this method of dividing, students will be making mental estimates. Students may find it helpful to make a list of multiplication facts for the divisor. Use questions like the following to guide students through the example:

- When you make the first estimate, what question must you ask yourself? *(How many 6s are in 354?)*
- Why is a multiple of 10 a good number to start with? *(because multiples of 10 are easy numbers to work with)*
- Where do you record your guesses (or partial quotients)? *(in a separate column to the right of the problem)*
- How do you find the final quotient (the answer) and where is it recorded? *(You find the sum of the partial quotients and record it below the column to the right of the problem.)*

Error Alert Watch for students who make the first estimate as if they were using the standard long-division algorithm—that is, looking at only the first two digits of the dividend. Remind students that when they're using this algorithm, they have to think about the whole number, not part of the number. So the first estimate will be an answer to the question, "How many equal groups of the divisor are in the *whole* dividend?"

Check Understanding

Have a volunteer go to the board and solve a division problem. Encourage the student to explain her or his strategy while working so that the class can follow along. Have students direct their questions to the volunteer, and guide that student in answering as necessary. If many students are confused about a particular aspect of the algorithm, do another problem on the board. When you are reasonably certain that most of your students understand the algorithm, assign the "Check Your Understanding" exercises at the bottom of page 63. For more difficult problems, refer students to pages 64 and 65. *(See answers in margin.)*

Page 63 Answer Key

1. 27
2. 92
3. 73
4. 3,365
5. 56
6. 68
7. 19
8. 149

Page 64 Answer Key

1. 21
2. 18
3. 24
4. 41
5. 25
6. 15
7. 23
8. 60

Page 65 Answer Key

1. 19
2. 18
3. 13
4. 27
5. 16 R9
6. 12 R4
7. 11 R4
8. 68

Name Date Time

Partial-Quotients Division (1-digit divisor)

FOCUS ALGORITHM

To find the number of 6s in 354, first find all the partial quotients. Record them in a column to the right of the problem. Then add the partial quotients to find the final quotient or answer.

Example

(dividend) (divisor)
354 ÷ 6

Ask: How many [6s] are in 354? (at least 50)
The first partial quotient is 50.
50 * 6 = 300
Subtract 300 from 354.

```
6)354
  300 | 50
   54 |
   54 |  9
    0   59
```

Ask: How many [6s] are in 54? (9)
The second partial quotient is 9.
9 * 6 = 54
Subtract 54 from 54.
The difference is 0, so there is no remainder.

Add the partial quotients. The answer is 59.

354 ÷ 6 = 59

Check Your Understanding

Solve the following problems.

1. 135 ÷ 5 **2.** 736 ÷ 8 **3.** 292 ÷ 4

4. 6,730 ÷ 2 **5.** 392 ÷ 7 **6.** 204 ÷ 3

7. 9)171 **8.** 6)894

Write your answers on a separate sheet of paper.

Name Date Time

FOCUS ALGORITHM

Partial-Quotients Division (2-digit divisor)

To find the number of 27s in 621, first find all the partial quotients. Record them in a column to the right of the problem. Then add the partial quotients to find the final quotient or answer.

Example

(dividend) (divisor)
621 ÷ 27

Ask: How many [27s] are in 621? (at least 20)
The first partial quotient is 20.
20 ∗ 27 = 540
Subtract 540 from 621.

```
27)621  |
   540  | 20
    81  |
    81  |  3
     0    23
```

Ask: How many [27s] are in 81? (3)
The second partial quotient is 3.
3 ∗ 27 = 81
Subtract 81 from 81.
The difference is 0, so there is no remainder.

Add the partial quotients. The answer is 23. **621 ÷ 27 = 23**

Check Your Understanding

Solve the following problems.

1. 273 ÷ 13 **2.** 342 ÷ 19 **3.** 768 ÷ 32

4. 902 ÷ 22 **5.** 425 ÷ 17 **6.** 630 ÷ 42

7. 36)828 **8.** 57)3,420

Division

 Write your answers on a separate sheet of paper.

Name Date Time

Partial-Quotients Division (2-digit divisor)

FOCUS ALGORITHM

To find the number of 12s in 238, first find all the partial quotients. Record them in a column to the right of the problem. Then add the partial quotients to find the final quotient or answer.

Example

(dividend) (divisor)
238 ÷ 12

Ask: How many [12s] are in 238? (at least 10)
The first partial quotient is 10.
10 * 12 = 120
Subtract 120 from 238.

Ask: How many [12s] are in 118? (9)
The second partial quotient is 9.
9 * 12 = 108
Subtract 108 from 118.
The difference is the remainder.

```
12)238  |
   120  | 10
   118  |
   108  |  9
    10    19
    ↑      ↑
Remainder  Quotient
```

Add the partial quotients to find the quotient.
The answer is 19 R10.

238 ÷ 12 → 19 R10

Check Your Understanding

Solve the following problems.

1. 380 ÷ 20 **2.** 720 ÷ 40 **3.** 663 / 51

4. 972 ÷ 36 **5.** 841 / 52 **6.** 64)772

7. 895 ÷ 81 **8.** 94)6,392

Write your answers on a separate sheet of paper.

U.S. Traditional Long Division (Standard) with Models

U.S. traditional long division (standard) is familiar to most adults and many children. The person using this algorithm places the dividend within a division bracket and the divisor to the left of the bracket. The problem solver then makes a series of educated multiplication / division estimates, records the result of each estimate underneath the dividend, and subtracts the result of each estimate from the number above it. If there is a remainder, the problem solver writes it next to the quotient.

The traditional method for teaching this algorithm is to begin with models (such as base-10 blocks), using them to demonstrate the process of dividing a dividend into equal groups.

Build Understanding

Divide the class into groups of four or five, provide each group with base-10 blocks, and direct each group to model the number 138 using the least number of blocks. When each group has built the correct model (consisting of 1 hundred, 3 tens, and 8 ones), ask students to divide the model into 6 equal groups. Allow each group to tackle the problem in its own way. If students seem confused about how to start, however, suggest that they think about regrouping or trading the largest block (the hundred) for 10 tens. Guide students as necessary until each group of students has successfully changed 1 hundred, 3 tens, and 8 ones into six equal groupings of 2 tens and 3 ones each.

Using page 67, explain that with this method of dividing, students will begin by making an estimate about what the first digit in the quotient (the answer) should be. Use questions like the following to guide students through the example:

- Why do you have to trade 3 hundreds for 30 tens? *(because 3 hundreds cannot be divided into 8 equal groups)*
- Why do you have to trade 1 ten for 10 ones? *(because 1 ten cannot be divided into 8 equal groups)*
- What does the last picture tell you? *(that 331 blocks are divided into 8 groups, 41 blocks are in each group, and 3 blocks are left over)*

Error Alert Watch for students who are multiplying incorrectly. Remind students that although the long-division process may seem complex, each multiplication step within the process is a simple, basic-fact step. Also, watch for students who are subtracting incorrectly. Suggest that these students cover the numbers above the numbers being subtracted with their index fingers to help them focus on only two numbers at a time—the two they are subtracting.

Check Understanding

Have students check each of their answers by multiplying the quotient by the divisor, adding the remainder if there is one, and then checking to see if the result matches the dividend. Have a volunteer go to the board and solve a division problem using the standard algorithm. Help the student describe the process while he or she works through it and correct any misconceptions as necessary, referring again to base-10 blocks or arrays if they seem to help. When you are reasonably certain that most of your students understand the algorithm, assign the "Check Your Understanding" exercises at the bottom of page 67. *(See answers in margin.)*

Page 67 Answer Key

1. 49

2. 63

3. 36

4. 82

5. 87

6. 83

7. 23 R7

8. 99 R3

Name Date Time

Long Division (Standard) with Models

Use base-10 blocks to model the dividend. Then make trades until you have the correct number of equal groups.

Example

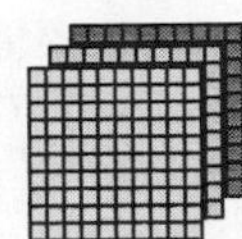

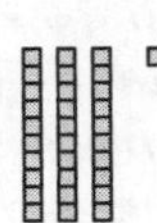

(dividend) (divisor)

331 ÷ 8

3 hundreds cannot be divided into 8 equal groups.
So rename 3 hundreds as 30 tens.

8)331

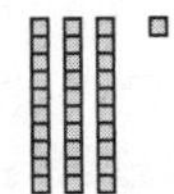

Divide 33 tens into 8 equal groups.
Each group has 4 tens, and 1 ten remains.

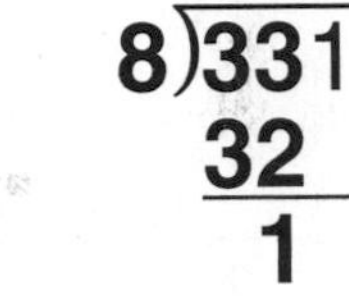

4
8)331
32
1

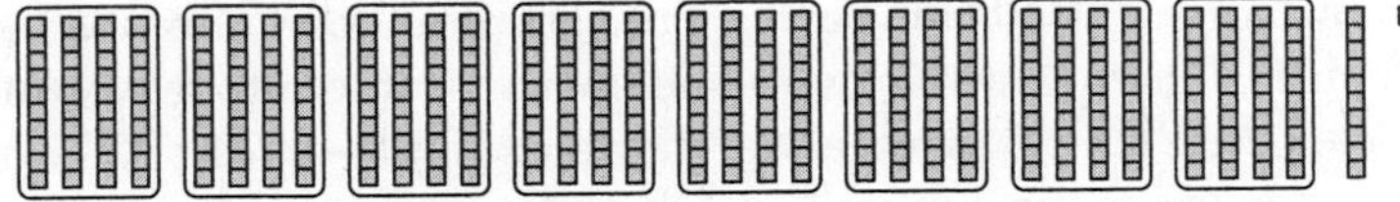

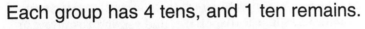

1 ten cannot be divided into 8 equal groups.
So rename 1 ten as 10 ones. There are now 11 ones.

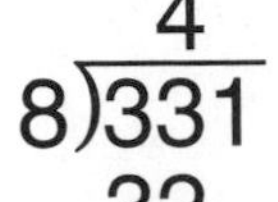

4
8)331
32
11

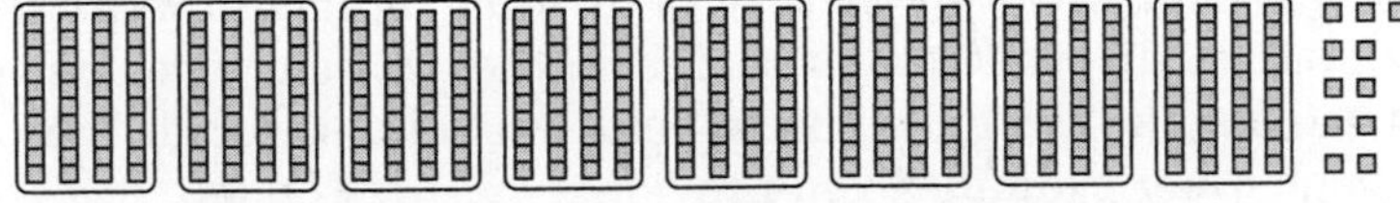

Divide 11 ones into 8 equal groups.
3 ones remain.

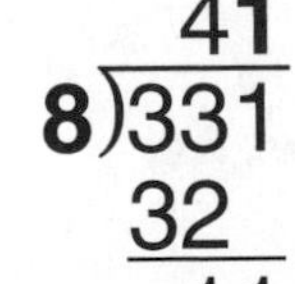

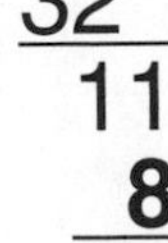

41
8)331
32
11
8
3

331 ÷ 8 → 41 R3

Check Your Understanding

Solve the following problems.

1. 5)245	**2.** 504 ÷ 8	**3.** 144 / 4	**4.** 574 ÷ 7
5. 3)261	**6.** 6)498	**7.** 214 / 9	**8.** 795 / 8

Write your answers on a separate sheet of paper.

U.S. Traditional Long Division (Standard)

U.S. traditional long division (standard) is familiar to most adults and many children. The person using this algorithm places the dividend within a division bracket and the divisor outside and to the left of the bracket. The problem solver then makes a series of educated multiplication / division estimates, records the result of each estimate underneath the dividend, and subtracts the result of each estimate from the number above it. If there is a remainder, the problem solver writes it next to the quotient.

The traditional method for teaching this algorithm is to begin with models (such as base-10 blocks) and then gradually move toward the use of symbols (that is, numerals) only.

Build Understanding

Review the process of making division estimates. Give students such problems as 48 ÷ 9; 77 ÷ 10; 82 ÷ 8; and 56 ÷ 6. Remind students to use a basic fact as the basis for each estimate, and explain that it is acceptable to have a number left over. Then write the following problem on the board: 312 ÷ 6. Have students estimate the first digit of the quotient, and remind them to use their basic-facts knowledge (their "fact power") to estimate how many 6s are in 31 *(5 with 1 left over).* Then work through the entire problem together on the board (312 ÷ 6 = 52). Finally, provide one more example—574 ÷ 7—and encourage students to exercise their mental-math skills when making estimates.

Note: Although the aim is to have students use mental math when estimating, allow those students who seem to be struggling with the process to write down their estimates, at least initially.

Using page 69, explain that with this method of dividing, students will begin by making an estimate about what the first digit in the quotient (the answer) should be. Use questions like the following to guide students through the example (and through other examples you provide):

- What will you multiply the divisor by to get a number as close to the first (two) digits as possible?
- How will you know if you have estimated correctly? *(Multiply the estimate by the divisor and then subtract the product from the first [two] digits. If the difference is greater than the divisor, then the estimate is too low—so try again!)*

Error Alert Watch for students who accept an estimate that is too low. If necessary, have students circle or highlight the divisor with a pen or pencil of another color to remind themselves to keep checking each remainder against the divisor.

Check Understanding

Divide students into pairs. Have one student in each pair solve a division problem orally, explaining each step as it is written on a sheet of paper. Have the person's partner listen and watch for errors and omissions. Then have partners exchange places and solve a second problem. When you are reasonably certain that most of your students understand the algorithm, assign the "Check Your Understanding" exercises at the bottom of page 69. *(See answers in margin.)*

Page 69 Answer Key

1. 43

2. 86

3. 99

4. 26

5. 85

6. 298

7. 571

8. 608 R2

Name Date Time

Long Division (Standard)

Estimate to find the first digit of the quotient. Write that digit correctly above the dividend and multiply it by the divisor. Write the product below in the dividend. Find the difference and bring down the next number in the dividend. Repeat the procedure until you have used all the digits in the dividend.

Example

3,843 ÷ 7

- **Think: How many 7s are in 38?** (5)
  Write 5 in the quotient, above the 8.
  Multiply 5 × 7. (35)
  Subtract 35 from 38. (3)
  Bring down the 4 from the dividend. (to make 34)
- **Think: How many 7s are in 34?** (4)
  Write 4 next to 5 in the quotient.
  Multiply 4 × 7. (28)
  Subtract 28 from 34. (6)
  Bring down the 3 from the dividend. (to make 63)
- **Think: How many 7s are in 63?** (9)
  Write 9 next to 4 in the quotient.
  Multiply 9 × 7. (63)
  Subtract 63 from 63. (0)

$$\begin{array}{r} 549 \\ 7\overline{)3{,}843} \\ \underline{35} \\ 34 \\ \underline{28} \\ 63 \\ \underline{63} \\ 0 \end{array}$$

3,843 ÷ 7 = 549

Check Your Understanding

Solve the following problems.

1. 172 ÷ 4 **2.** $5\overline{)430}$ **3.** $2\overline{)198}$

4. 182 ÷ 7 **5.** $9\overline{)765}$ **6.** 894 ÷ 3

7. 4,568 / 8 **8.** 3,042 ÷ 5

Write your answers on a separate sheet of paper.

Column Division

Column division connects a manipulative-based approach to paper-and-pencil. Making this connection allows students to conceptually understand the division process as they move to the symbolic level. This process encourages students to utilize base-10 blocks and language that breaks the dividend into separate digits. For example, 583 would focus on 5 things, 8 things, and 3 things rather than 583 items. The student breaks each part into hundreds, tens, and ones, with only one place value being considered at a time.

Even those students whose basic-facts knowledge and estimation skills are limited can find correct answers using this approach to division. In the process, students can move from the concrete to the paper-and-pencil level once they feel comfortable. This graphic column presentation greatly reduces error.

Build Understanding

Divide the class into groups of three. Provide each group with base-10 blocks and direct them to model the number 53 (5 tens, 3 ones). Tell students that the blocks represent 53 pieces of candy and direct them to divide the pieces equally among two students. When dividing the 5 longs among 2 students, the groups should see that they have to exchange one long for ten ones. The groups should determine that each student would receive 26 pieces of candy with 1 left over.

The sharing of base-10 blocks at each place value is the conceptual basis for this division algorithm. Explain that it is best to always begin with the largest base-10 blocks. If they can't be shared evenly, they should be exchanged for smaller base-10 blocks, as in the example above.

Using page 71, walk students through an example of the column-division algorithm.

Error Alert Watch for students who do not trade in one of the longs for 10 ones when dividing 53 into 2 groups. Do another example with these students to make sure they understand the process of equal grouping.

Check Understanding

Give each group 2 or 3 additional problems to solve. Encourage each student to explain his or her strategy while working so that the small group can follow along. If many students are confused about a particular aspect of the algorithm, do another problem as a whole class. When you are reasonably certain that most of your students understand the algorithm, assign the "Check Your Understanding" exercises at the bottom of page 71. *(See answers in margin.)*

Page 71 Answer Key

1. 151 R2

2. 121

3. 76

4. 66 R3

5. 208

6. 1,975 R1

7. 1,340 R3

8. 537 R11

Name Date Time

Column Division

In the example below, think of sharing $583 among 4 people.

1. Draw lines to separate the digits in the dividend. Work left to right. Begin in the left column.

4) 5	8	3

2. Think of the 5 in the hundreds column as 5 $100 bills to be shared by 4 people. Each person gets 1 $100 bill. There is 1 $100 bill remaining.

1		
4) 5	8	3
− 4		
1		

3. Trade the 1 $100 bill for 10 $10 bills. Think of the 8 in the tens column as 8 $10 bills. That makes 10 + 8 = 18 $10 bills in all.

1		
4) 5	~~8~~	3
− 4	18	
~~1~~		

4. If 4 people share 18 $10 bills, each person gets 4 $10 bills. There are 2 $10 bills remaining.

1	4	
4) 5	~~8~~	3
− 4	18	
~~1~~	− 16	
	2	

5. Trade the 2 $10 bills for 20 $1 bills. Think of the 3 in the ones column as 3 $1 bills. That makes 20 + 3 = 23 $1 bills.

1	4	
4) 5	~~8~~	~~3~~
− 4	18	23
~~1~~	− 16	
	~~2~~	

6. If 4 people share 23 $1 bills, each person gets 5 $1 bills. There are 3 $1 bills remaining.

   Record the answer as 145 R3.
   Each person receives $145 and $3 are left over.

1	4	5
4) 5	~~8~~	~~3~~
− 4	18	23
~~1~~	− 16	− 20
	~~2~~	3

Check Your Understanding

Solve the following problems.

1. 455 ÷ 3 **2.** 726 ÷ 6 **3.** 532 / 7 **4.** 267 / 4

5. 832 / 4 **6.** 3,951 ÷ 2 **7.** 6,703 / 5 **8.** 8,603 / 16

Write your answers on a separate sheet of paper.

Column Division for Decimals

Column division for whole numbers can easily be applied to the division of decimals. When this algorithm is applied to decimals, the student must first think of a power of 10 that, when multiplied by the divisor, will change the divisor into a whole number. Once both divisor and dividend have been adjusted by the same power of 10, division can take place as it does with whole numbers.

Build Understanding

If students need to review the whole-number version of this algorithm, refer them to page 71. Review multiplying decimals by powers of 10. Then give students numbers like 0.5, 0.03, and 0.0008, and ask them by what power of 10 they would multiply each number to make it a whole number.

Using page 73, tell students to begin multiplying both the divisor and the dividend by the power of 10 that makes the divisor a whole number. Explain to students that this process creates an equivalent problem. Fractional equivalents might help students see that this is true: 0.324 / 0.04 (multiplied by 10) = 3.24 / 0.4 (multiplied by 10) = 32.4 / 4. Use questions like the following to guide students through the example:

- By which power of 10 would you multiply 0.04 to make it a whole number? *(100)*
- Which number do you place to the left of the division bracket? *(4)*
- Will you need to make any trades before you share? *(Yes. Trade 3 tens for 30 ones.)*
- Where do you place the decimal point in your answer? *(above the decimal point in the dividend; 8.1)*

Error Alert Watch for students who multiply the divisor and the dividend by different powers of 10. Make sure that students select the power of 10 based on the divisor and that they multiply both the divisor and the dividend by that power of 10.

Check Understanding

Have a volunteer go to the board and model the column algorithm for decimal division for the problem 6.74 ÷ 0.5. Encourage the student to explain what he or she is doing while working so that the class can follow along. Have students direct their questions to the volunteer, and guide that student in answering as necessary. If many students are confused about a particular aspect of the algorithm, do another problem on the board. When you are reasonably certain that most students understand the algorithm, assign the "Check Your Understanding" exercises at the bottom of page 73. Notice that Exercise 7 involves a 2-digit divisor. Exercise 8 requires students to insert a zero between the decimal point and the first digit in the quotient. *(See answers in margin.)*

Page 73 Answer Key

1. 120.1

2. 0.15

3. 0.87

4. 1,490

5. 61

6. 1.62

7. 21.5

8. 0.0182

Name Date Time

Column Division for Decimals

Think of a power of 10 that will make the divisor a whole number. Multiply both the divisor and the dividend by the same power of ten. Then divide as you would for whole numbers. Remember to correctly place the decimal point in the quotient.

Example

(dividend) (divisor)

$0.324 \div 0.04$

Multiply both the divisor and the dividend by a power of 10 to make the divisor a whole number.

$0.324 * 100 = 32.4$

$0.04 * 100 = 4$

Write the new problem.

4) 3 | 2. | 4

Trade the 3 tens for 30 ones. That makes 30 + 2 ones in all. **Record** 32 in the ones column.

4) ~~3~~ | ~~2~~. 32 | 4

Place a decimal point in the quotient directly above the one in the dividend.

There are 8[4s] in 32. **Record** 8 in the answer space. **Record** 32 in the ones column. Subtract.

8.
4) ~~3~~ | ~~2~~. 32 − 32 | 4

There is 1[4] in 4. **Record** 1 in the answer space. **Record** 4 in the tenths column. Subtract.

8. 1
4) ~~3~~ | ~~2~~. 32 − 32 0 | 4 − 4 0

$0.324 \div 0.04 = 8.1$

Check Your Understanding

Solve the following problems.

1. $36.03 \div 0.3$ **2.** $0.0075 \div 0.05$ **3.** 0.0261 / 0.03 **4.** 0.006)8.94

5. 2.44 / 0.04 **6.** $0.0486 \div 0.03$ **7.** 40.85 / 1.9 **8.** 0.3)0.00546

Write your answers on a separate sheet of paper.

U.S. Traditional Long Division for Decimals (Standard)

U.S. traditional long division (standard) is familiar to most adults and many children. When applied to decimals, the problem solver must first think of a power of 10 that, when multiplied by the divisor, will change the divisor into a whole number. Once both divisor and dividend have been adjusted by the same power of 10, division can take place as it does with whole numbers.

Build Understanding

If students need to review the whole-number version of this algorithm, refer them to page 69.

Review multiplying decimals by powers of 10. Then give students numbers like 0.3, 0.09, and 0.006, and ask them by what power of 10 they would multiply each number to make it a whole number.

Using page 75, tell students to begin by multiplying both the divisor and the dividend by the power of 10 that makes the divisor a whole number. Explain to students that this process creates an equivalent problem. Fractional equivalents might help students see that this is true: $0.216 \div 0.06 = 2.16 \div 0.6 = 21.6 \div 6$.

Use questions like the following to guide students through the example:

- By which power of 10 would you multiply 0.06 to make it a whole number? *(100)*
- Which number do you place to the left of the division bracket? *(6)*
- Which multiplication fact can help you estimate the first digit of the quotient? *($3 \times 6 = 18$)*
- Where do you place the decimal point in your answer? *(above the decimal point in the dividend; 3.6)*

Error Alert Watch for students who multiply the divisor and dividend by different powers of 10. Make sure that students select the power of 10 based on the *divisor* and that they then multiply *both* the divisor and the dividend by that power of 10.

Check Understanding

Have a volunteer go to the board and model the long (standard) division algorithm for the problem $36.5 \div 0.5$. Encourage the student to explain what he or she is doing while working so that the class can follow along. Have students direct their questions to the volunteer, and guide that student in answering as necessary. If many students are confused about a particular aspect of the algorithm, do another problem on the board. When you are reasonably certain that most of your students understand the algorithm, assign the "Check Your Understanding" exercises at the bottom of page 75. Notice that Exercise 8 requires students to insert a zero between the decimal point and the first digit in the quotient. *(See answers in margin.)*

Page 75 Answer Key

1. 2.7

2. 8.2

3. 19

4. 0.87

5. 15

6. 5.9

7. 0.79

8. 0.0624

Name Date Time

Long Division for Decimals (Standard)

Think of a power of 10 that will make the divisor a whole number. Multiply both the divisor and dividend by the same power of 10.

Then divide as you would with whole numbers. Remember to correctly place the decimal point in the quotient.

Example

(dividend) (divisor)
$0.216 \div 0.06$

Decide which power of 10 multiplied by the divisor will make the divisor a whole number.

$0.06 * 100 = 6$

Multiply both the divisor and the dividend by this power of 10.

$0.216 * 100 = 21.6$

Write the result as a division problem with a division bracket.

Divide as you would with whole numbers.

Place a decimal point in the quotient directly above the one in the dividend.

```
   3.6
6)21.6
  18
   36
   36
    0
```

$0.216 \div 0.06 = 3.6$

Check Your Understanding

Solve the following problems.

1. $0.108 \div 0.04$ **2.** 5.74 / 0.7 **3.** 0.9)17.1

4. 0.03)0.0261 **5.** 0.075 / 0.005 **6.** $4.72 \div 0.8$

7. 0.474 / 0.6 **8.** $0.02496 \div 0.4$

Write your answers on a separate sheet of paper.

Division

Converting Common Fractions to Decimals

In order to convert common fractions to decimals, students use a procedure that requires dividing the numerator of the fraction by the denominator. Students using the Everyday Mathematics® *program have solved division problems written as fractions since fourth grade. The numerator is the dividend of the problem and the denominator is the divisor of the problem. Some fractions require adding a decimal point and one or more zeros to the dividend in order to carry out the division process.*

Build Understanding

Review the process of making division estimates. Give students such problems as $45 \div 8 =$, $88 \div 10 =$, and so on. Remind students to use a basic fact as the basis for the estimate. Then write $\frac{1}{4}$ on the board. Explain to students that this fraction can be written as a division problem. Rewrite this fraction writing the dividend (1) within a division bracket and the divisor (4) outside to the left of the bracket. Place a decimal point to the right of the dividend, and attach two zeros after the last digit of the dividend. Then work through the entire problem together on the board. $1 \div 4 = 0.25$, or $\frac{1}{4} = 0.25$.

Using page 77, explain how to convert the common fraction $\frac{1}{6}$ to a decimal. Use questions like the following to guide students through this procedure.

- How do I rewrite this problem using the division bracket?
- Why do we attach zeros to the dividend?
- How many zeros did you need to attach for this problem?

Error Alert Watch for students who attach zeros and place the decimal incorrectly. Also look for students who switch around the divisor (denominator) and dividend (numerator) when writing the problem with the division bracket. Watch to make sure students drop down the zeros as needed.

Check Understanding

Select a volunteer to come up to the board to work through another problem. While the student records on the board encourage the class to follow along with their own recordings. Students should ask the volunteer questions if they do not understand the procedure. Work through additional examples as needed. When you are reasonably certain that most students understand the procedure, assign the "Check Your Understanding" exercises at the bottom of page 77. *(See answers in margin.)*

Page 77 Answer Key

1. 0.75

2. 0.8

3. 0.875

4. $0.\overline{3}$

5. 0.4

6. 0.625

7. $0.\overline{4}$

8. $0.\overline{714285}$

Division

Name Date Time

Converting Common Fractions to Decimals

Write the fraction as a division problem using the division bracket. (Write the numerator as the dividend and the denominator as the divisor.) Place a decimal point after the dividend and attach zeros. As you divide, record the quotient above the dividend.

Example Convert to a decimal. $\frac{1}{6}$

Write the fraction using the division bracket. Place a decimal after the dividend and attach two zeros.

$$6\overline{)1.00}$$

How many 6s are in 10? **Record** the answer in the tenths place. Bring down the next zero.

$$\begin{array}{r} .16 \\ 6\overline{)1.00} \\ \underline{6\downarrow} \\ 40 \\ \underline{36} \\ 4 \end{array}$$

How many 6s are in 40? **Record** the answer in the hundredths place. Since there is still a remainder, attach one more zero to the dividend. Bring down the zero.

Continue to divide until you see a pattern. (The 6 will continue to repeat in the quotient.)

$$\begin{array}{r} .166 \\ 6\overline{)1.000} \\ \underline{6\downarrow} \\ 40 \\ \underline{36\downarrow} \\ 40 \\ \underline{36} \\ 4 \end{array} = .16$$

This type of common fraction converts into a repeating decimal. Write this by placing a bar over the first 6 to indicate it will repeat.

$$\frac{1}{6} = .1\overline{6}$$

Check Your Understanding

Convert the following fractions to decimals.

1. $\frac{3}{4}$ **2.** $\frac{4}{5}$ **3.** $\frac{7}{8}$ **4.** $\frac{1}{3}$

5. $\frac{2}{5}$ **6.** $\frac{5}{8}$ **7.** $\frac{4}{9}$ **8.** $\frac{5}{7}$

Write your answers on a separate sheet of paper.

Fraction Division (with Models)

Consider a typical whole-number division problem like 41 ÷ 3. People often solve it by thinking about how many 3s are in 41. The same thought process applies to the division of fractions, and when used in combination with fraction models, it helps students gain meaningful understanding of dividing fractions.

Build Understanding

Have students use graph paper or templates to draw fraction models. As a review, ask students to represent fractions like $\frac{1}{2}$, $\frac{1}{3}$, $\frac{1}{6}$, and $\frac{2}{3}$. Encourage students to use a variety of shapes, such as squares, circles, hexagons, and triangles. Ask students how they would represent a whole number, such as 5.

Using page 79, explain that students will use models to show the division. In Example 1, thinking about pizzas can help students visualize how many $\frac{1}{3}$s are in 5. If you have 5 pizzas, and divide each pizza into $\frac{1}{3}$s, then you have 15 portions. In Example 2, if you have $\frac{1}{2}$ of a pizza and want portions in $\frac{1}{6}$s, you divide the whole pizza into portions, each one the size of $\frac{1}{6}$ of a pizza. You end up with 3 portions. Use questions like the following to guide students through the examples:

- How do you represent the dividend? *(Draw the number of shapes needed — whole shapes for whole numbers and a part of a shape for any fraction less than 1.)*
- How would you divide each unit? *(Divide each unit into the number of equal pieces identified by the divisor.)*
- How do you find the quotient? *(Count the total number of pieces.)*

Error Alert Watch for students with inaccurate drawings, especially when both the dividend and the divisor are fractions. Remind students that they need to divide each *whole unit shape* into the number of equal pieces identified by the divisor.

Check Understanding

Have students work in pairs, and instruct partners to take turns drawing models. Circulate around the room checking drawings. Then work through a couple of additional examples if necessary. When you are reasonably certain that most of your students understand the algorithm, assign the "Check Your Understanding" exercises at the bottom of page 79. *(See answers in margin.)*

Page 79 Answer Key

1. 8

2. 4

3. 2

4. 2

5. 12

6. 16

7. 4

8. $\frac{2}{3}$

Name Date Time

Fraction Division (with Models)

Draw a picture or pictures to show the dividend. Then draw lines to show division of each unit by the divisor. Count the parts to find the quotient.

Example 1

(dividend) (divisor)

$5 \div \frac{1}{3}$

Show 5.

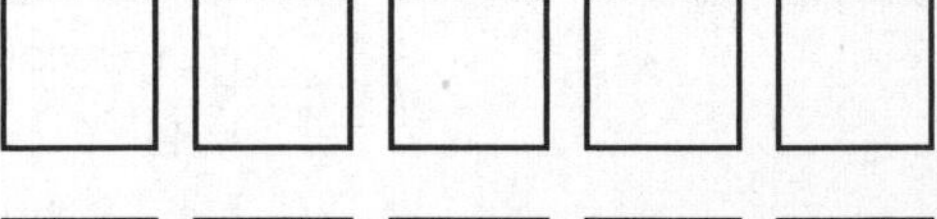

Draw lines or trade pieces to show the division of each unit by $\frac{1}{3}$.

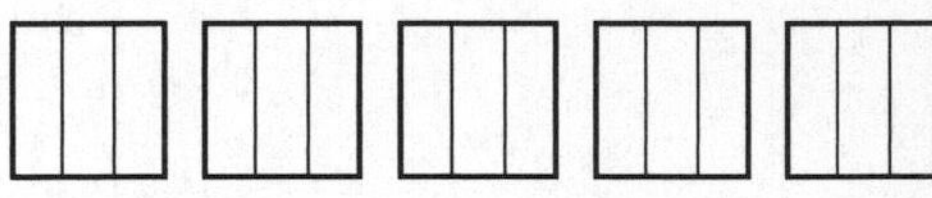

There are 15 $\frac{1}{3}$s in 5.

$$5 \div \frac{1}{3} = 15$$

Example 2

$\frac{1}{2} \div \frac{1}{6}$

Show $\frac{1}{2}$.

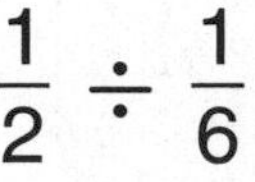

Draw lines or trade pieces to show the division of the whole unit by $\frac{1}{6}$.

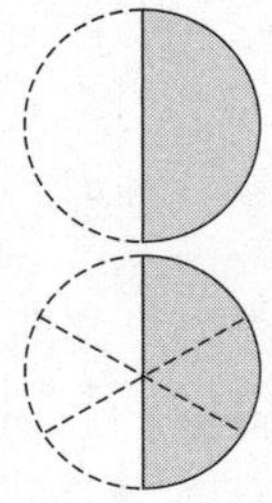

There are 3 $\frac{1}{6}$s in $\frac{1}{2}$.

$$\frac{1}{2} \div \frac{1}{6} = 3$$

Check Your Understanding

Solve the following problems.

1. $4 \div \frac{1}{2}$ **2.** $\frac{1}{2} \div \frac{1}{8}$ **3.** $\frac{1}{3} \div \frac{1}{6}$ **4.** $\frac{1}{5} \div \frac{1}{10}$

5. $3 \div \frac{1}{4}$ **6.** $2 \div \frac{1}{8}$ **7.** $\frac{2}{3} \div \frac{1}{6}$ **8.** $\frac{1}{3} \div \frac{1}{2}$

Write your answers on a separate sheet of paper.

Fraction Division

To divide two fractions, problem solvers multiply the first fraction by the reciprocal of the second fraction. In the Everyday Mathematics® *program, this is called the Division of Fractions Property, and it is based on several mathematical rules regarding fractions and the reciprocal relationship between multiplication and division.*

Build Understanding

Review finding reciprocals. Remind students that they need to rename whole numbers and mixed numbers as fractions before they can find their reciprocals. Ask students to find the reciprocal of $\frac{1}{3}$ *(3)*, 7 *($\frac{1}{7}$)*, $2\frac{2}{3}$ *($\frac{3}{8}$)*, and $\frac{5}{6}$ *($\frac{6}{5}$, or $1\frac{1}{5}$)*.

Using the example $\frac{1}{6} \div \frac{3}{2}$, walk students through the steps below so that they understand why the Division of Fractions Property works.

- Multiply the first fraction by the reciprocal of the second fraction. $\frac{1}{6} \div \frac{3}{2} = \frac{1}{6} \times \frac{2}{3}$
- Simplify as needed. $= \frac{2}{18}$, or $\frac{1}{9}$

Use the example $2\frac{3}{4} \div 11$ to explain the division of mixed numbers.

- Change any whole number or mixed number to an improper fraction. $2\frac{3}{4} \div 11 = \frac{11}{4} \div \frac{11}{1}$
- Multiply the first fraction by the reciprocal of the second fraction. $= \frac{11}{4} \times \frac{1}{11}$
- Simplify as needed. $= \frac{11}{44} = \frac{1}{4}$

Error Alert Watch for students who use incorrect reciprocals or just change the problem from division to multiplication without using reciprocals. You may want to have students write and label the reciprocal of each divisor before they begin each problem.

Check Understanding

Divide the class into groups of 3 or 4 and assign a leader in each group to explain the steps in the examples. Tell group members to direct their questions to their group leader. When you are reasonably certain that most of your students understand the algorithm, assign the "Check Your Understanding" exercises at the bottom of page 81. *(See answers in margin.)*

Page 81
Answer Key

1. $\frac{2}{3}$
2. $\frac{1}{6}$
3. 16
4. $\frac{1}{6}$
5. $\frac{2}{9}$
6. 6
7. 15
8. $1\frac{1}{2}$

Name Date Time

Fraction Division

Use the Division of Fractions Property to divide. That is, to find the quotient of two fractions, multiply the first fraction by the reciprocal of the second fraction.

Division of Fractions Property

$$\frac{a}{b} \div \frac{c}{d} = \frac{a}{b} * \frac{d}{c}$$

Example 1

$$\frac{4}{5} \div \frac{2}{3}$$

Multiply the first fraction by the reciprocal of the second fraction.

$$\frac{4}{5} * \frac{3}{2} = \frac{12}{10} = 1\frac{2}{10}, \text{ or } \mathbf{1\frac{1}{5}}$$

Simplify as needed.

Example 2

$$4 \div 1\frac{1}{3}$$

Rename whole numbers or mixed numbers as improper fractions.

$$\frac{4}{1} \div \frac{4}{3}$$

Multiply the first fraction by the reciprocal of the second fraction.

$$\frac{4}{1} * \frac{3}{4} = \frac{12}{4} = \mathbf{3}$$

Check Your Understanding

Solve the following problems.

1. $\frac{1}{3} \div \frac{1}{2}$

2. $\frac{2}{3} \div 4$

3. $6 \div \frac{3}{8}$

4. $\frac{1}{8} \div \frac{3}{4}$

5. $\frac{1}{6} \div \frac{3}{4}$

6. $4 \div \frac{2}{3}$

7. $9 \div \frac{3}{5}$

8. $1\frac{7}{8} \div 1\frac{1}{4}$

Write your answers on a separate sheet of paper.

Practice Sets

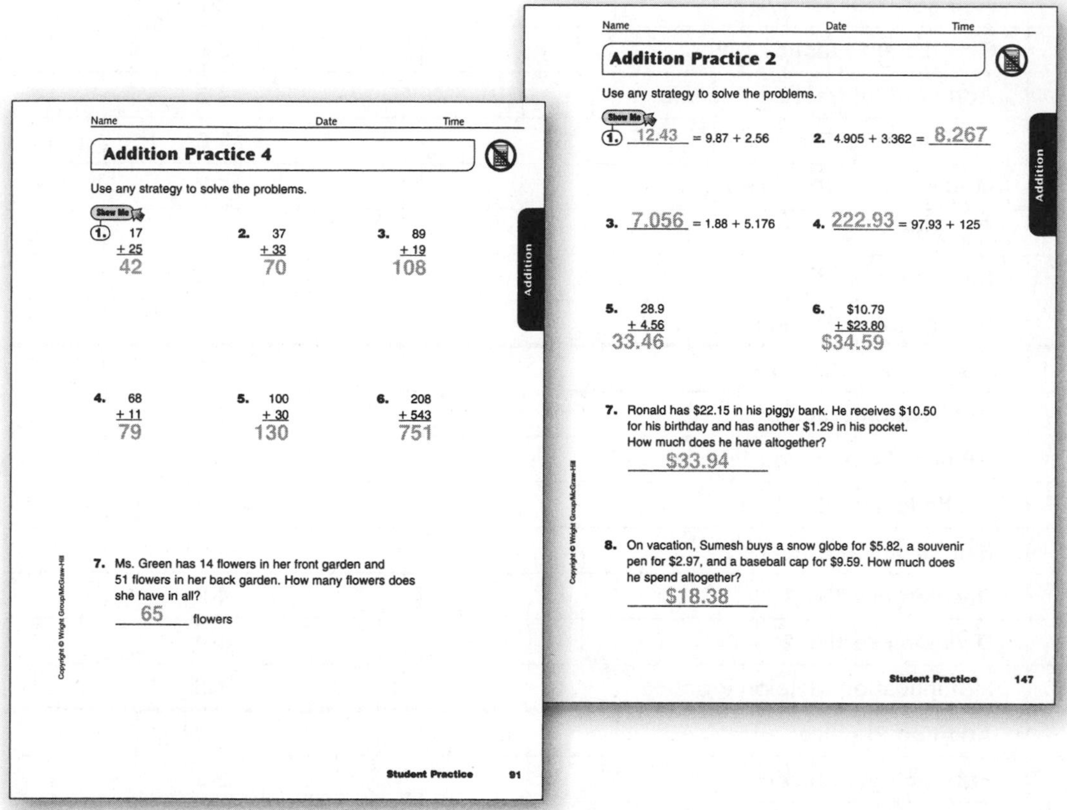

Name Date Time

Addition Practice 4

Use any strategy to solve the problems.

Show Me

1. 17 + 25 = 42
2. 37 + 33 = 70
3. 89 + 19 = 108
4. 68 + 11 = 79
5. 100 + 30 = 130
6. 208 + 543 = 751
7. Ms. Green has 14 flowers in her front garden and 51 flowers in her back garden. How many flowers does she have in all?
   65 flowers

Addition

Copyright © Wright Group/McGraw-Hill

Student Practice 91

Name Date Time

Addition Practice 2

Use any strategy to solve the problems.

Show Me

1. 12.43 = 9.87 + 2.56
2. 4.905 + 3.362 = 8.267
3. 7.056 = 1.88 + 5.176
4. 222.93 = 97.93 + 125
5. 28.9 + 4.56 = 33.46
6. $10.79 + $23.80 = $34.59
7. Ronald has $22.15 in his piggy bank. He receives $10.50 for his birthday and has another $1.29 in his pocket. How much does he have altogether?
   $33.94
8. On vacation, Sumesh buys a snow globe for $5.82, a souvenir pen for $2.97, and a baseball cap for $9.59. How much does he spend altogether?
   $18.38

Addition

Copyright © Wright Group/McGraw-Hill

Student Practice 147

Practice Set Correlation Chart

Grade Level	Practice Set(s)	Use After This Lesson in the *Teacher's Lesson Guide*
2	Addition Practice 1–5	4-9
2	Subtraction Practice 1, 2	6-5
2	Subtraction Practice 3–5	11-3
3	Addition Practice 1, 2	2-7
3	Subtraction Practice 1, 2	2-8
3	Addition/Subtraction Practice 1–3	2-8
3	Multiplication Practice 1	9-4
3	Multiplication Practice 2	9-5
3	Multiplication Practice 3	9-12
4	Addition Practice 1, 2	2-7
4	Subtraction Practice 1, 2	2-9
4	Addition/Subtraction Practice	4-5
4	Multiplication Practice 1	5-6
4	Multiplication Practice 2	5-7
4	Division Practice 1	6-3
4	Division Practice 2	6-10
4	Multiplication/Division Practice	9-9
5	Addition Practice 1, 2	2-2
5	Subtraction Practice 1, 2	2-3
5	Addition/Subtraction Practice	2-3
5	Multiplication Practice 1	2-8
5	Multiplication Practice 2	2-9
5	Division Practice 1	4-2
5	Division Practice 2	4-4
5	Multiplication/Division Practice	4-5
6	Addition Practice	2-3
6	Subtraction Practice	2-3
6	Addition/Subtraction Practice	2-3
6	Multiplication Practice 1	2-5
6	Multiplication Practice 2	2-6
6	Division Practice 1	2-7
6	Division Practice 2	2-8
6	Multiplication/Division Practice 1	2-7
6	Multiplication/Division Practice 2, 3	2-8

Name Date Time

Addition Practice 1

Use any strategy to solve the problems.

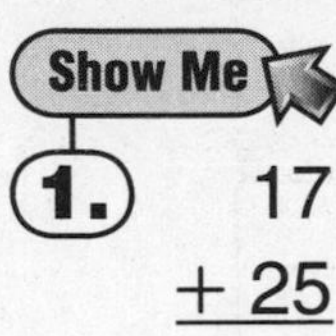

1. $\begin{array}{r} 17 \\ +\ 25 \\ \hline \end{array}$

2. $\begin{array}{r} 11 \\ +\ 20 \\ \hline \end{array}$

3. $\begin{array}{r} 30 \\ +\ 50 \\ \hline \end{array}$

4. $\begin{array}{r} 68 \\ +\ 31 \\ \hline \end{array}$

5. $\begin{array}{r} 55 \\ +\ 14 \\ \hline \end{array}$

6. $\begin{array}{r} 87 \\ +\ 37 \\ \hline \end{array}$

7. Shawn has 65 superhero stickers and 32 animal stickers. How many stickers does he have in all?

    ____________ stickers

Addition

Answers to Addition Practice 1

While these problems may be appropriate for **second-grade** students, feel free to assign some or all of them to any student who needs practice at this level.

Recommended Use Use any time after Lesson 4-9 in Grade 2.

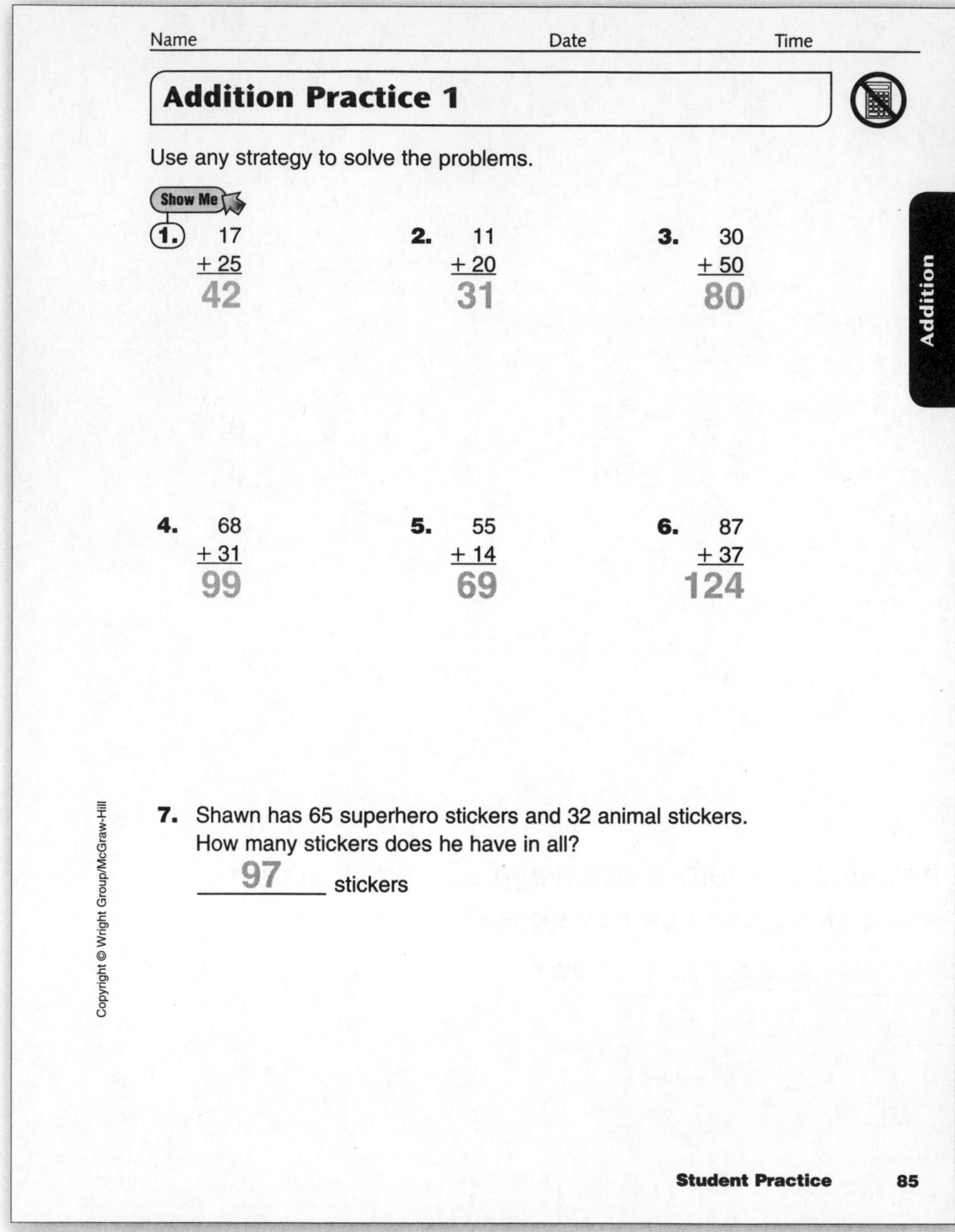

Name Date Time

Addition Practice 1

Use any strategy to solve the problems.

Show Me

1. 17 + 25 = 42

2. 11 + 20 = 31

3. 30 + 50 = 80

4. 68 + 31 = 99

5. 55 + 14 = 69

6. 87 + 37 = 124

7. Shawn has 65 superhero stickers and 32 animal stickers. How many stickers does he have in all?
97 stickers

Student Practice 85

Addition

Name Date Time

Addition Practice 2

Use any strategy to solve the problems.

1. 26 + 5

2. 48 + 33

3. 56 + 24

4. 91 + 11

5. 505 + 39

6. 866 + 107

7. Audrey counts 143 pebbles in her turtle's tank. Her mother adds a bag of 120 pebbles. How many pebbles are in the tank now?

_____________ pebbles

Answers to Addition Practice 2

While these problems may be appropriate for **second-grade** students, feel free to assign some or all of them to any student who needs practice at this level.

Recommended Use Use any time after Lesson 4-9 in Grade 2.

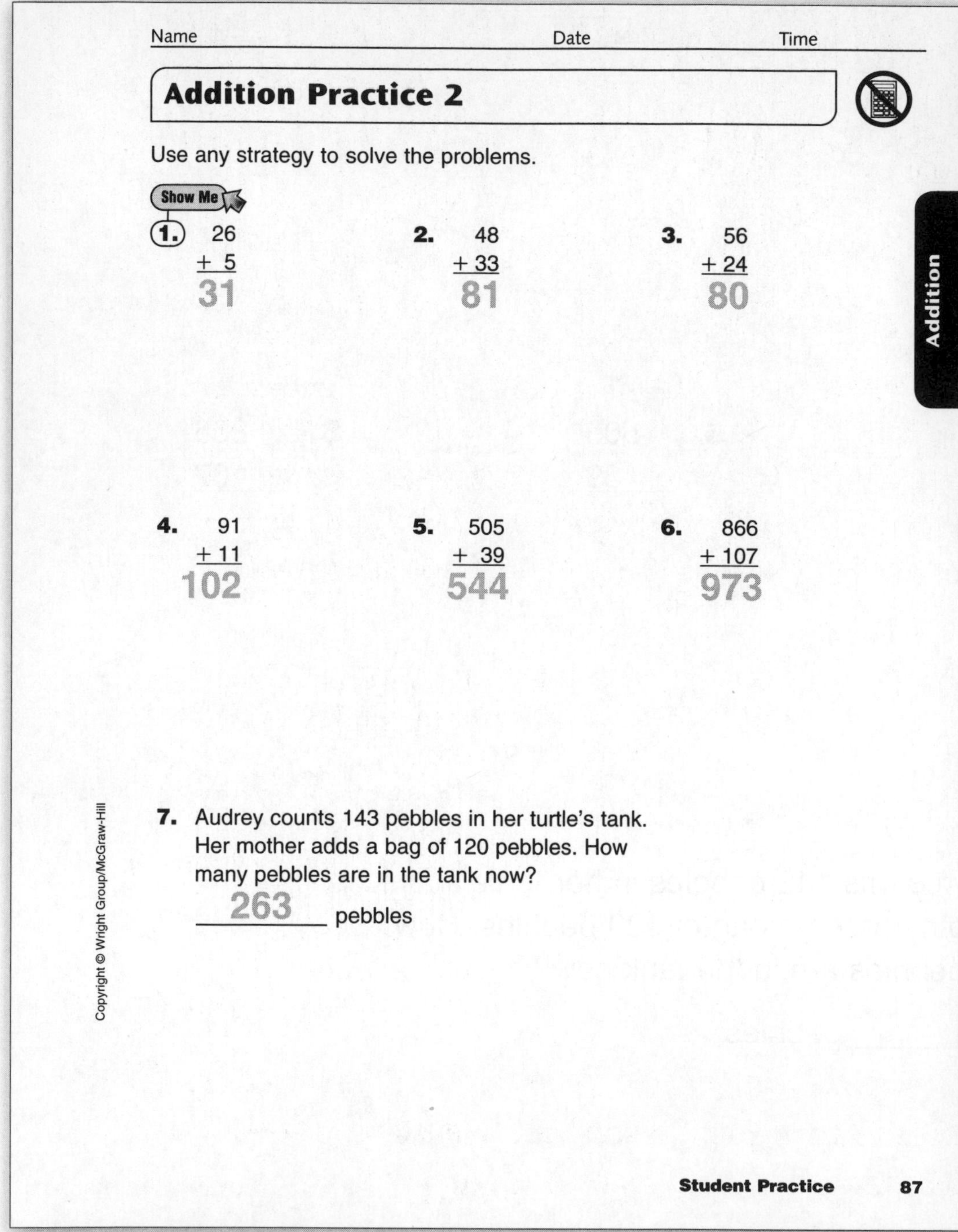

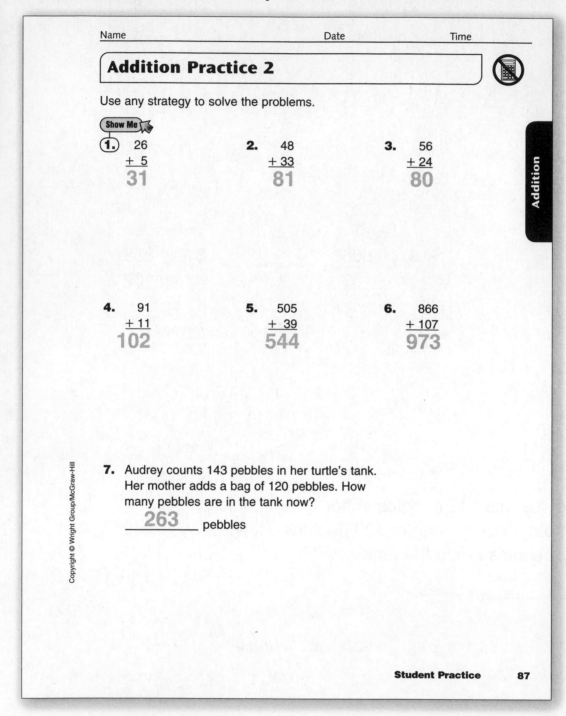

Name Date Time

Addition Practice 2

Use any strategy to solve the problems.

Show Me

1. 26 + 5 = 31

2. 48 + 33 = 81

3. 56 + 24 = 80

4. 91 + 11 = 102

5. 505 + 39 = 544

6. 866 + 107 = 973

7. Audrey counts 143 pebbles in her turtle's tank. Her mother adds a bag of 120 pebbles. How many pebbles are in the tank now?

263 pebbles

Name Date Time

Addition Practice 3

Use any strategy to solve the problems.

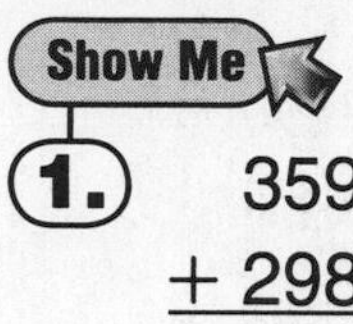

1. 359
+ 298

2. 78
+ 24

3. 64
+ 31

4. 197
+ 75

5. 382
+ 49

6. 532
+ 191

7. Carlo's aquarium has 13 goldfish and 9 angel fish. How many fish does he have in all?

_______ fish

Addition

Answers to Addition Practice 3

While these problems may be appropriate for **second-grade** students, feel free to assign some or all of them to any student who needs practice at this level.

Recommended Use Use any time after Lesson 4-9 in Grade 2.

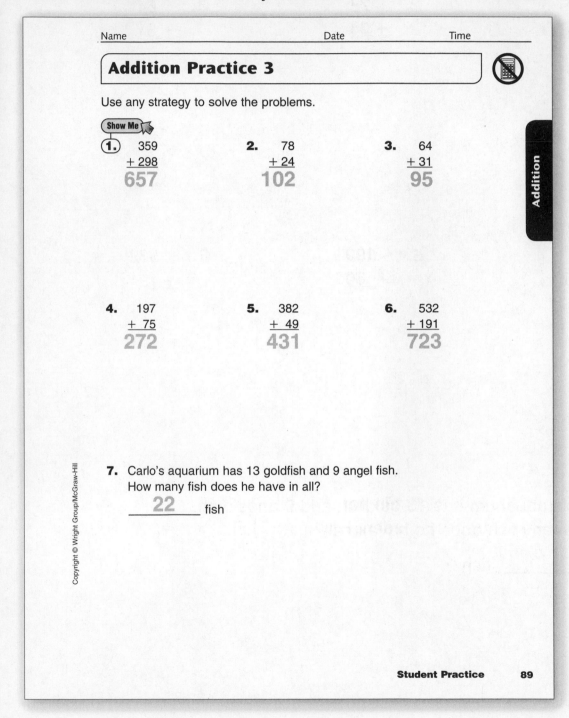

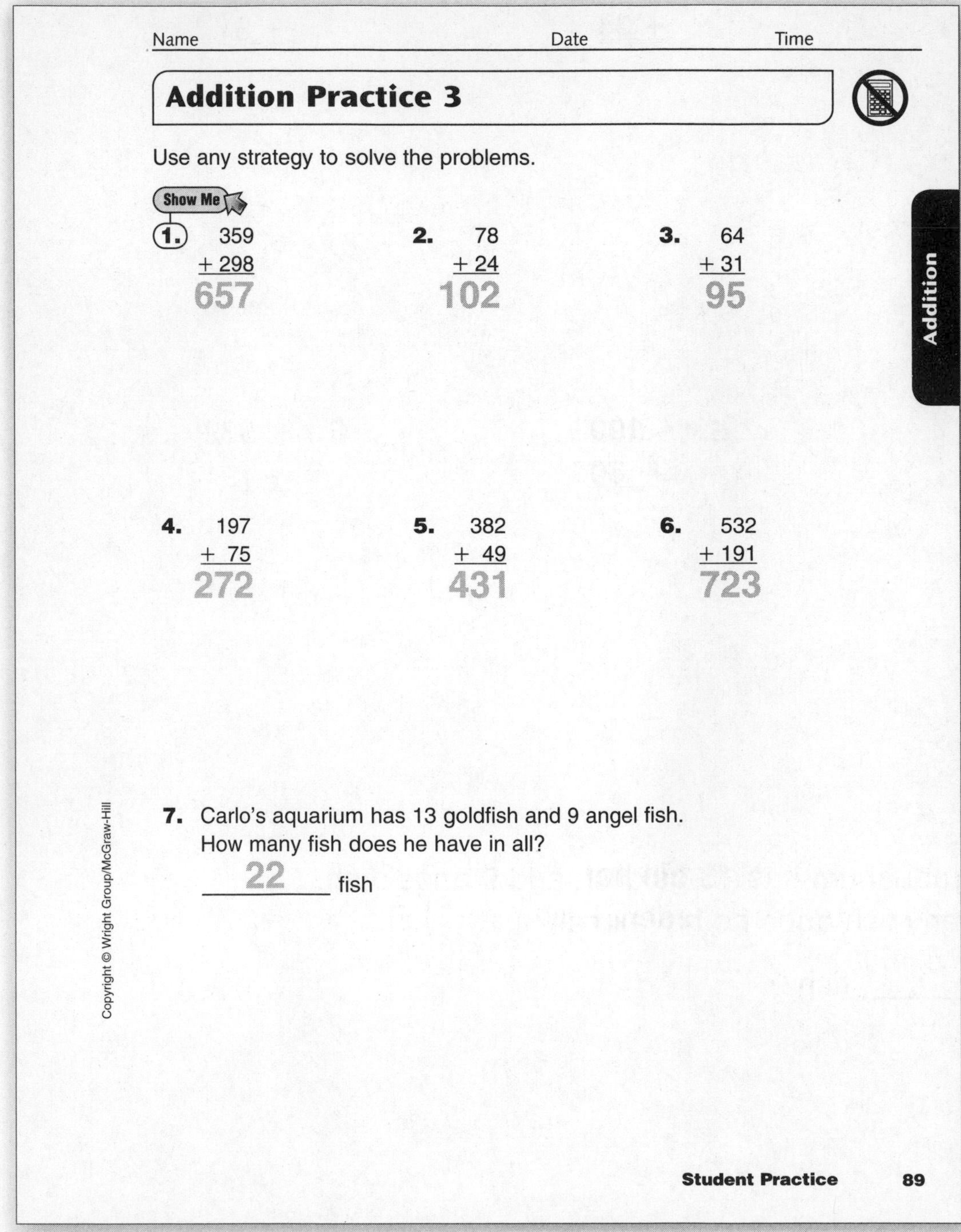
Name Date Time

Addition Practice 3

Use any strategy to solve the problems.

Show Me

1. 359 + 298 = **657**

2. 78 + 24 = **102**

3. 64 + 31 = **95**

4. 197 + 75 = **272**

5. 382 + 49 = **431**

6. 532 + 191 = **723**

7. Carlo's aquarium has 13 goldfish and 9 angel fish. How many fish does he have in all?
22 fish

Student Practice 89

Name Date Time

Addition Practice 4

Use any strategy to solve the problems.

1. $\begin{array}{r} 17 \\ +\ 25 \\ \hline \end{array}$

2. $\begin{array}{r} 37 \\ +\ 33 \\ \hline \end{array}$

3. $\begin{array}{r} 89 \\ +\ 19 \\ \hline \end{array}$

4. $\begin{array}{r} 68 \\ +\ 11 \\ \hline \end{array}$

5. $\begin{array}{r} 100 \\ +\ 30 \\ \hline \end{array}$

6. $\begin{array}{r} 208 \\ +\ 543 \\ \hline \end{array}$

7. Ms. Green has 14 flowers in her front garden and 51 flowers in her back garden. How many flowers does she have in all?

   ____________ flowers

Addition

Answers to Addition Practice 4

While these problems may be appropriate for **second-grade** students, feel free to assign some or all of them to any student who needs practice at this level.

Recommended Use Use any time after Lesson 4-9 in Grade 2.

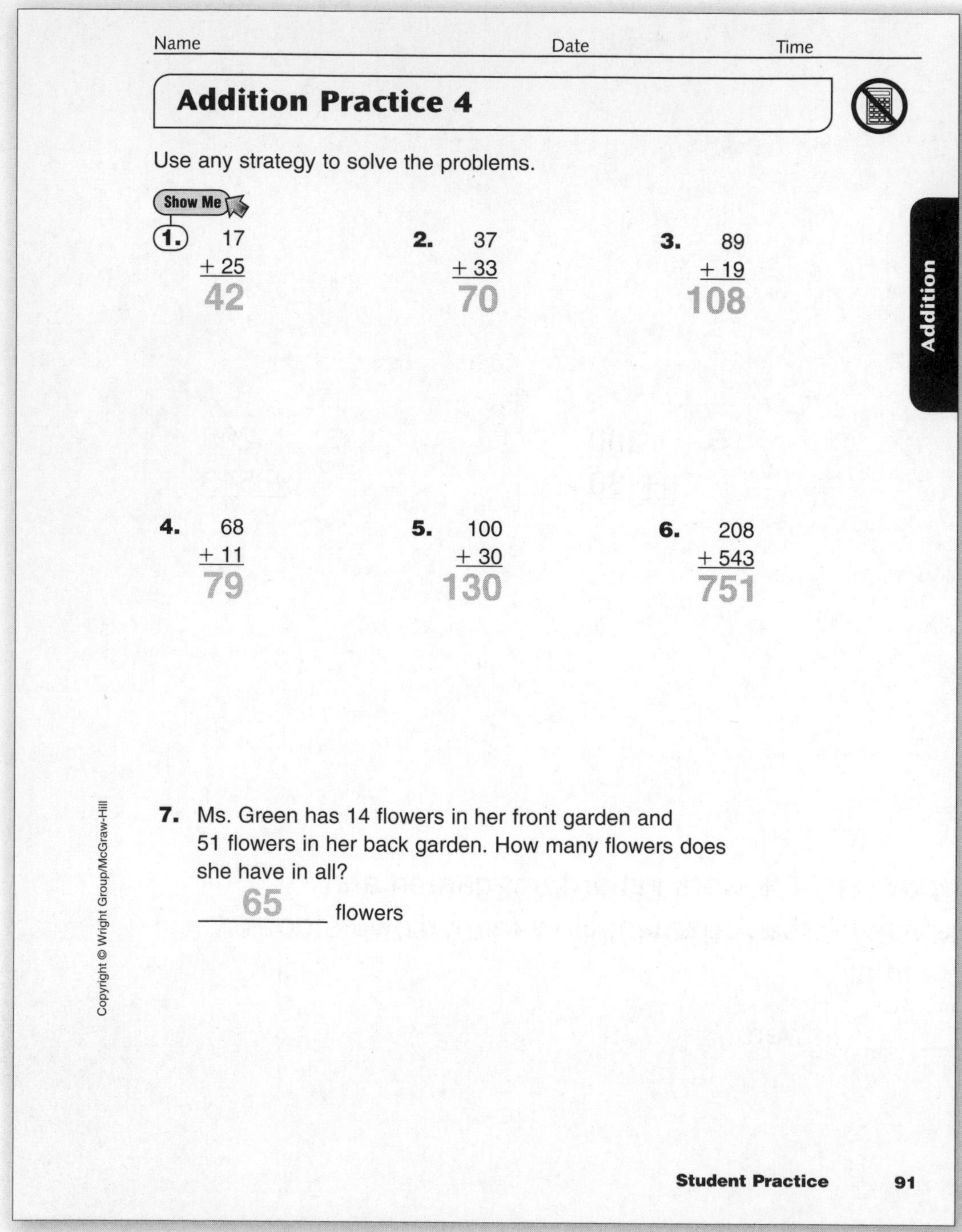

Name Date Time

Addition Practice 4

Use any strategy to solve the problems.

Show Me

1. 17 + 25 = **42**

2. 37 + 33 = **70**

3. 89 + 19 = **108**

4. 68 + 11 = **79**

5. 100 + 30 = **130**

6. 208 + 543 = **751**

7. Ms. Green has 14 flowers in her front garden and 51 flowers in her back garden. How many flowers does she have in all?

65 flowers

Addition

Name Date Time

Addition Practice 5

Use any strategy to solve the problems.

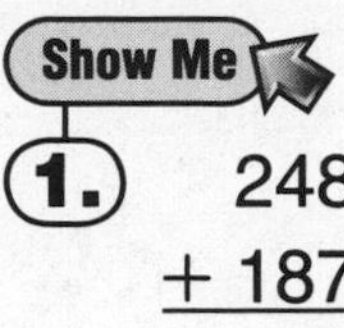

1. 248 + 187

2. 87 + 12

3. 504 + 88

4. 49 + 15

5. 408 + 115

6. 371 + 476

7. Nick has 97 pennies in his bank. His father gives him 41 more. How many pennies does he have now?

_____________ pennies

Addition

Answers to Addition Practice 5

While these problems may be appropriate for **second-grade** students, feel free to assign some or all of them to any student who needs practice at this level.

Recommended Use Use any time after Lesson 4-9 in Grade 2.

Addition

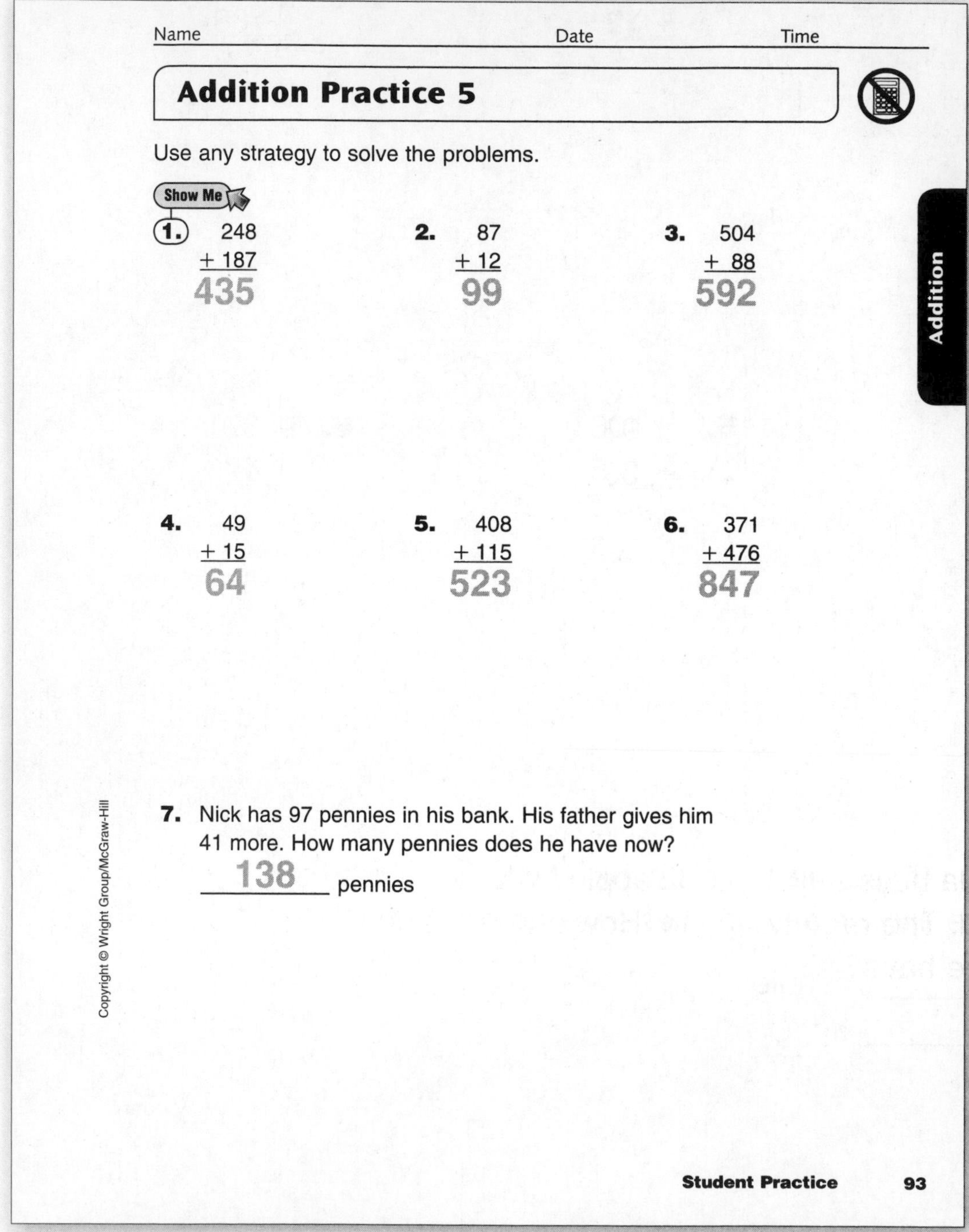

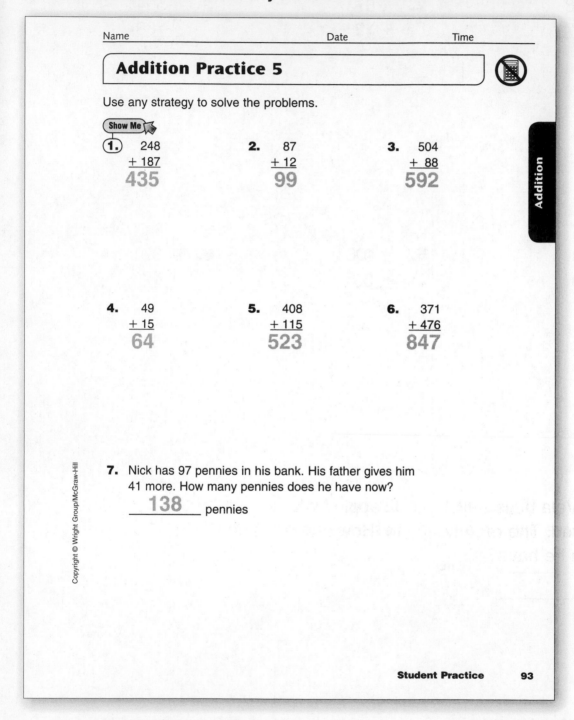

Name Date Time

Addition Practice 5

Use any strategy to solve the problems.

Show Me

1. 248 + 187 = 435

2. 87 + 12 = 99

3. 504 + 88 = 592

4. 49 + 15 = 64

5. 408 + 115 = 523

6. 371 + 476 = 847

7. Nick has 97 pennies in his bank. His father gives him 41 more. How many pennies does he have now?
138 pennies

Student Practice 93

Name Date Time

Subtraction Practice 1

Use any strategy to solve the problems.

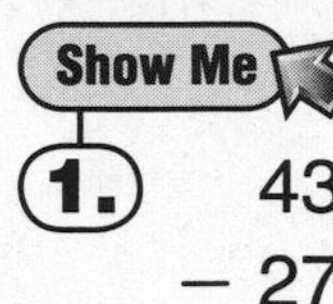

1. 43 − 27

2. 78 − 12

3. 83 − 23

4. 79 − 50

5. 99 − 33

6. 44 − 39

Subtraction

7. Mr. Vela buys a crate of 32 apples. 11 of the apples are red. The rest are green. How many green apples does he have?

____________ apples

Answers to Subtraction Practice 1

While these problems may be appropriate for **second-grade** students, feel free to assign some or all of them to any student who needs practice at this level.

Recommended Use Use any time after Lesson 6-5 in Grade 2.

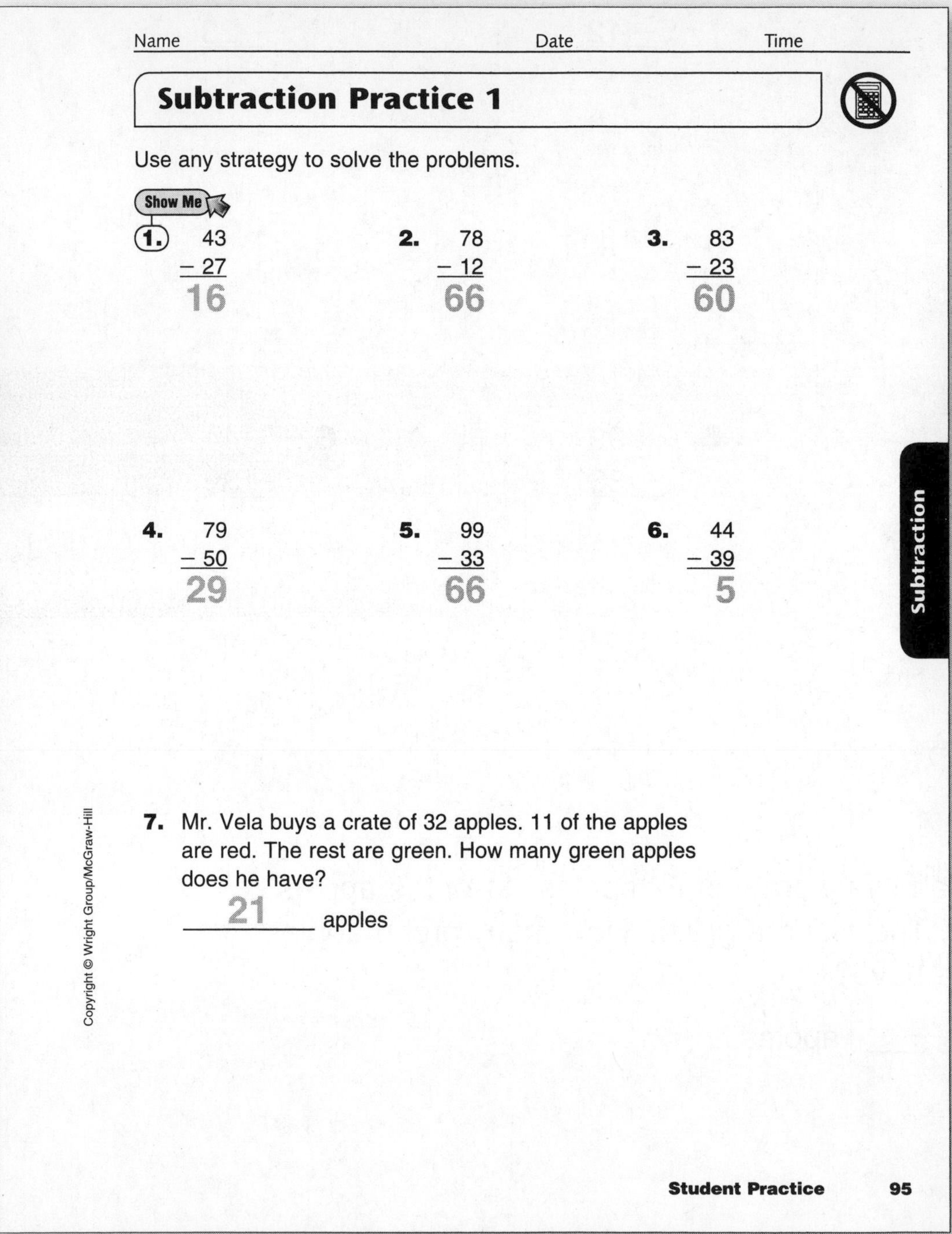

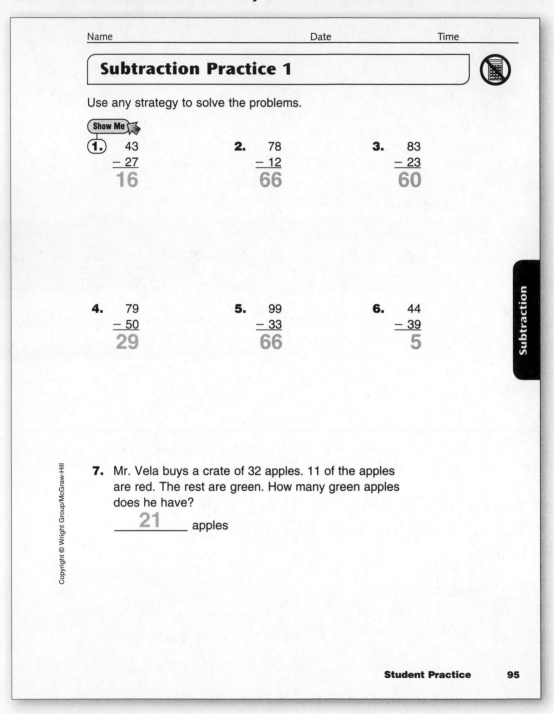

Name Date Time

Subtraction Practice 1

Use any strategy to solve the problems.

Show Me

1. 43 − 27 = **16**

2. 78 − 12 = **66**

3. 83 − 23 = **60**

4. 79 − 50 = **29**

5. 99 − 33 = **66**

6. 44 − 39 = **5**

7. Mr. Vela buys a crate of 32 apples. 11 of the apples are red. The rest are green. How many green apples does he have?

21 apples

Subtraction

Student Practice 95

Name Date Time

Subtraction Practice 2

Use any strategy to solve the problems.

1. $\begin{array}{r} 43 \\ -\ 27 \\ \hline \end{array}$

2. $\begin{array}{r} 57 \\ -\ 40 \\ \hline \end{array}$

3. $\begin{array}{r} 88 \\ -\ 31 \\ \hline \end{array}$

4. $\begin{array}{r} 76 \\ -\ 32 \\ \hline \end{array}$

5. $\begin{array}{r} 27 \\ -\ 14 \\ \hline \end{array}$

6. $\begin{array}{r} 73 \\ -\ 54 \\ \hline \end{array}$

7. Halley has 73 bottle caps in her collection. She gives 12 of them to her friend Anna. How many does she have now?

_____________ bottle caps

Subtraction

Answers to Subtraction Practice 2

While these problems may be appropriate for **second-grade** students, feel free to assign some or all of them to any student who needs practice at this level.

Recommended Use Use any time after Lesson 6-5 in Grade 2.

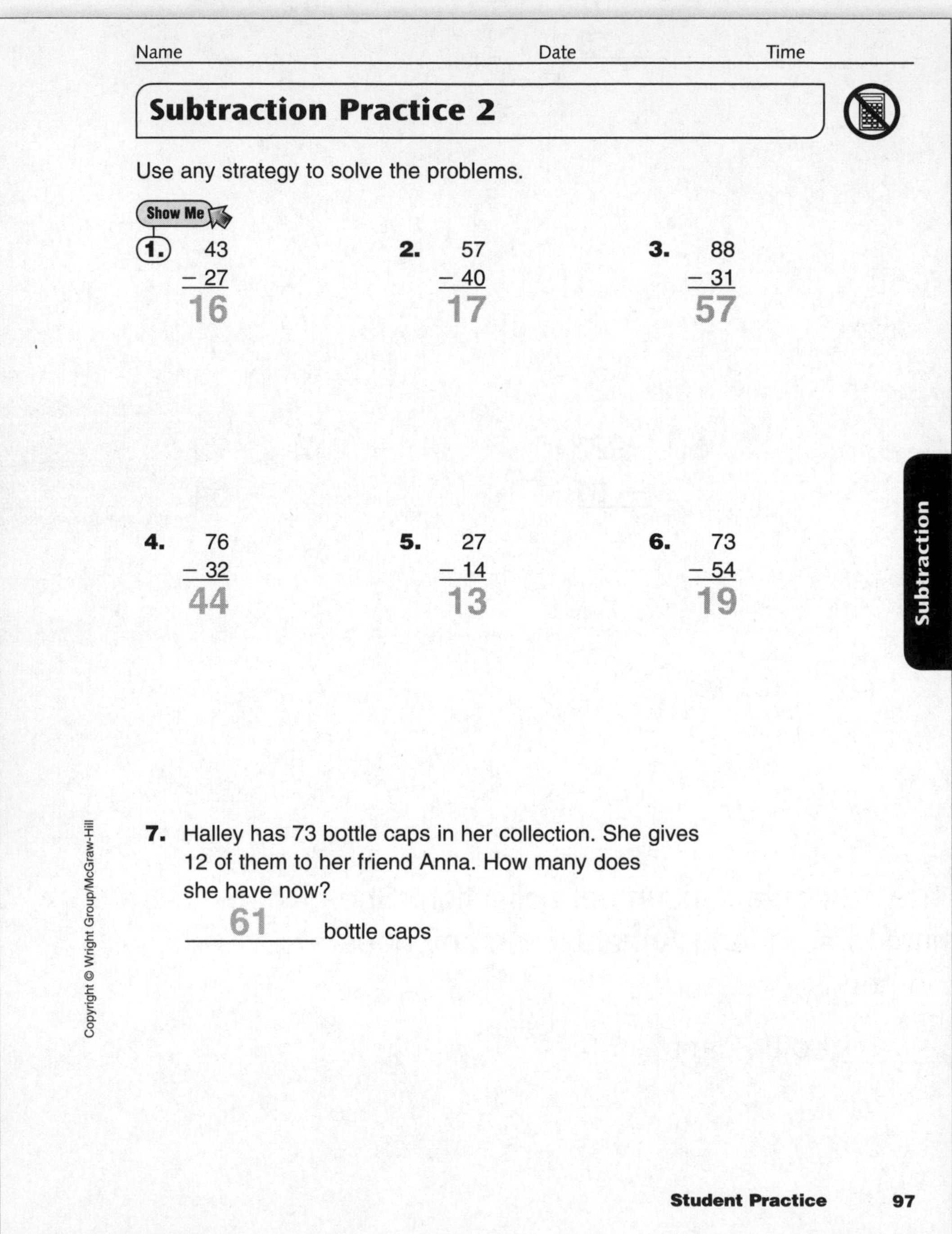

Name Date Time

Subtraction Practice 2

Use any strategy to solve the problems.

Show Me

1. 43 − 27 = **16**

2. 57 − 40 = **17**

3. 88 − 31 = **57**

4. 76 − 32 = **44**

5. 27 − 14 = **13**

6. 73 − 54 = **19**

7. Halley has 73 bottle caps in her collection. She gives 12 of them to her friend Anna. How many does she have now?

61 bottle caps

Subtraction

Student Practice 97

Subtraction

Name Date Time

Subtraction Practice 3

Use any strategy to solve the problems.

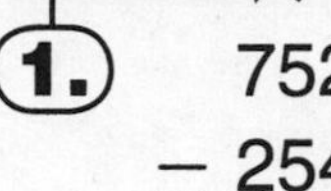

1. 752
 − 254

2. 78
 − 13

3. 54
 − 29

4. 36
 − 17

5. 923
 − 61

6. 856
 − 367

Subtraction

7. Luke finds 27 shells on the beach. He gives 16 of them to his sister. How many does he have now?

 ________ shells

Answers to Subtraction Practice 3

While these problems may be appropriate for **second-grade** students, feel free to assign some or all of them to any student who needs practice at this level.

Recommended Use Use any time after Lesson 11-3 in Grade 2.

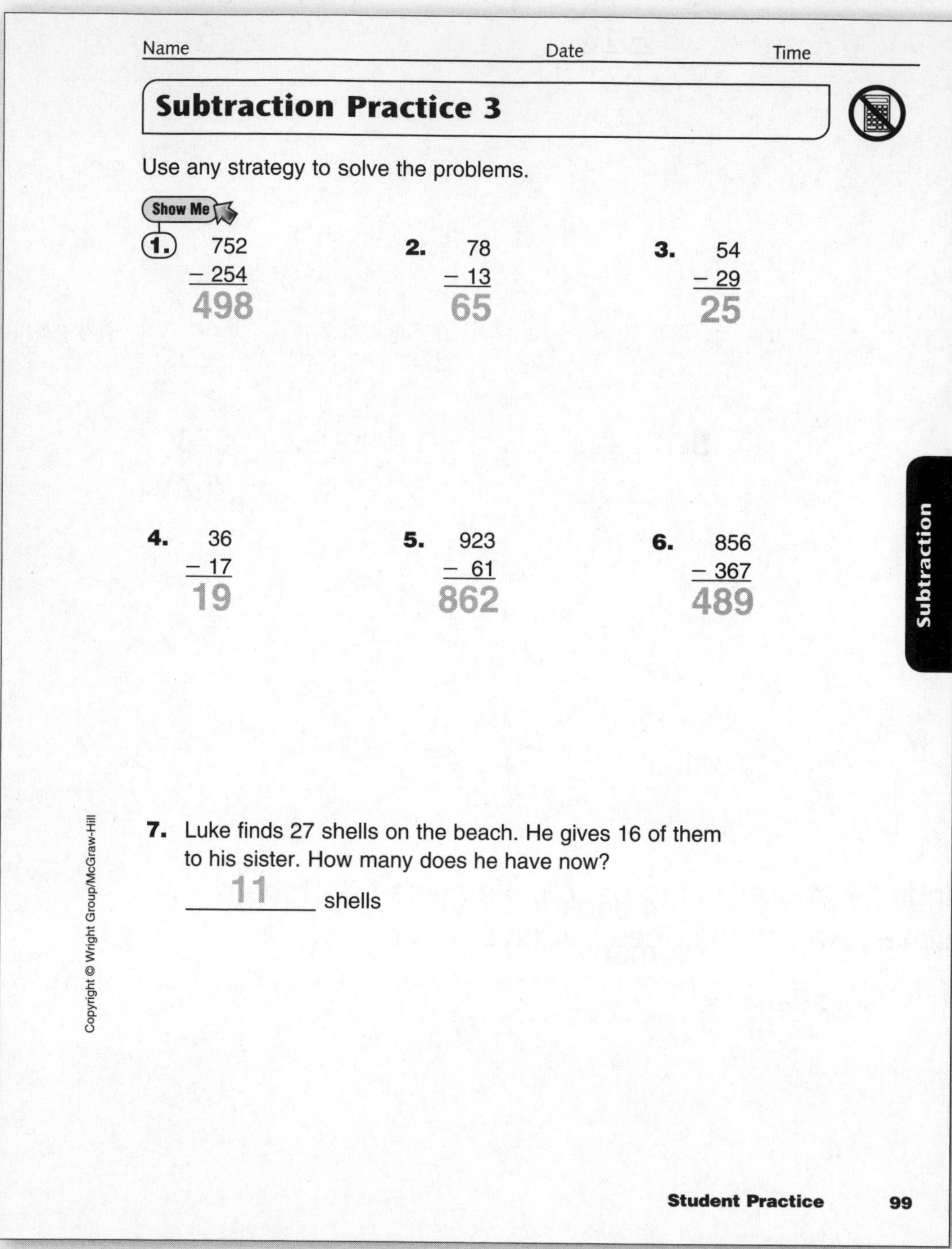

Name Date Time

Subtraction Practice 3

Use any strategy to solve the problems.

Show Me

1. 752 − 254 = **498**

2. 78 − 13 = **65**

3. 54 − 29 = **25**

4. 36 − 17 = **19**

5. 923 − 61 = **862**

6. 856 − 367 = **489**

7. Luke finds 27 shells on the beach. He gives 16 of them to his sister. How many does he have now?

11 shells

Subtraction

Student Practice 99

Name Date Time

Subtraction Practice 4

Use any strategy to solve the problems.

1. $\begin{array}{r} 352 \\ -\ 168 \\ \hline \end{array}$

2. $\begin{array}{r} 66 \\ -\ 29 \\ \hline \end{array}$

3. $\begin{array}{r} 42 \\ -\ 27 \\ \hline \end{array}$

4. $\begin{array}{r} 133 \\ -\ 24 \\ \hline \end{array}$

5. $\begin{array}{r} 705 \\ -\ 38 \\ \hline \end{array}$

6. $\begin{array}{r} 563 \\ -\ 104 \\ \hline \end{array}$

7. Maria makes a batch of 24 cookies. She puts chocolate chips in 15 of them. How many cookies do not have chocolate chips?

   ____________ cookies

Subtraction

Answers to Subtraction Practice 4

While these problems may be appropriate for **second-grade** students, feel free to assign some or all of them to any student who needs practice at this level.

Recommended Use Use any time after Lesson 11-3 in Grade 2.

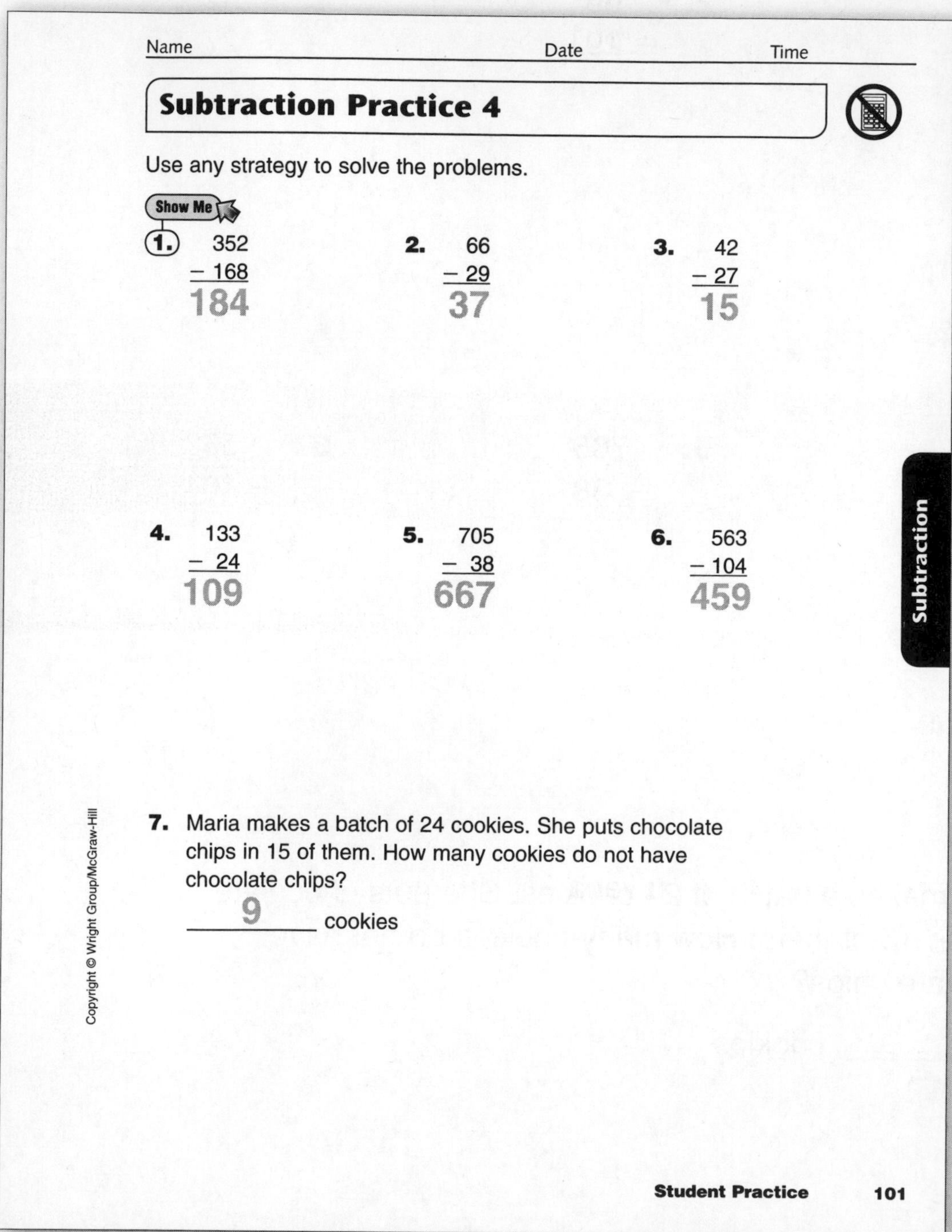

Name Date Time

Subtraction Practice 4

Use any strategy to solve the problems.

Show Me

1. 352 − 168 = 184

2. 66 − 29 = 37

3. 42 − 27 = 15

4. 133 − 24 = 109

5. 705 − 38 = 667

6. 563 − 104 = 459

7. Maria makes a batch of 24 cookies. She puts chocolate chips in 15 of them. How many cookies do not have chocolate chips?

9 cookies

Subtraction

Student Practice 101

Subtraction

Name Date Time

Subtraction Practice 5

Use any strategy to solve the problems.

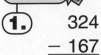

1.
$$\begin{array}{r} 324 \\ -\ 167 \\ \hline \end{array}$$

2.
$$\begin{array}{r} 854 \\ -\ 101 \\ \hline \end{array}$$

3.
$$\begin{array}{r} 132 \\ -\ 15 \\ \hline \end{array}$$

4.
$$\begin{array}{r} 892 \\ -\ 229 \\ \hline \end{array}$$

5.
$$\begin{array}{r} 362 \\ -\ 109 \\ \hline \end{array}$$

6.
$$\begin{array}{r} 817 \\ -\ 738 \\ \hline \end{array}$$

7. Olivia takes 22 pictures on vacation. Her sister Danise takes 35. How many more pictures does Danise take than Olivia?

__________ pictures

Subtraction

Answers to Subtraction Practice 5

While these problems may be appropriate for **second-grade** students, feel free to assign some or all of them to any student who needs practice at this level.

Recommended Use Use any time after Lesson 11-3 in Grade 2.

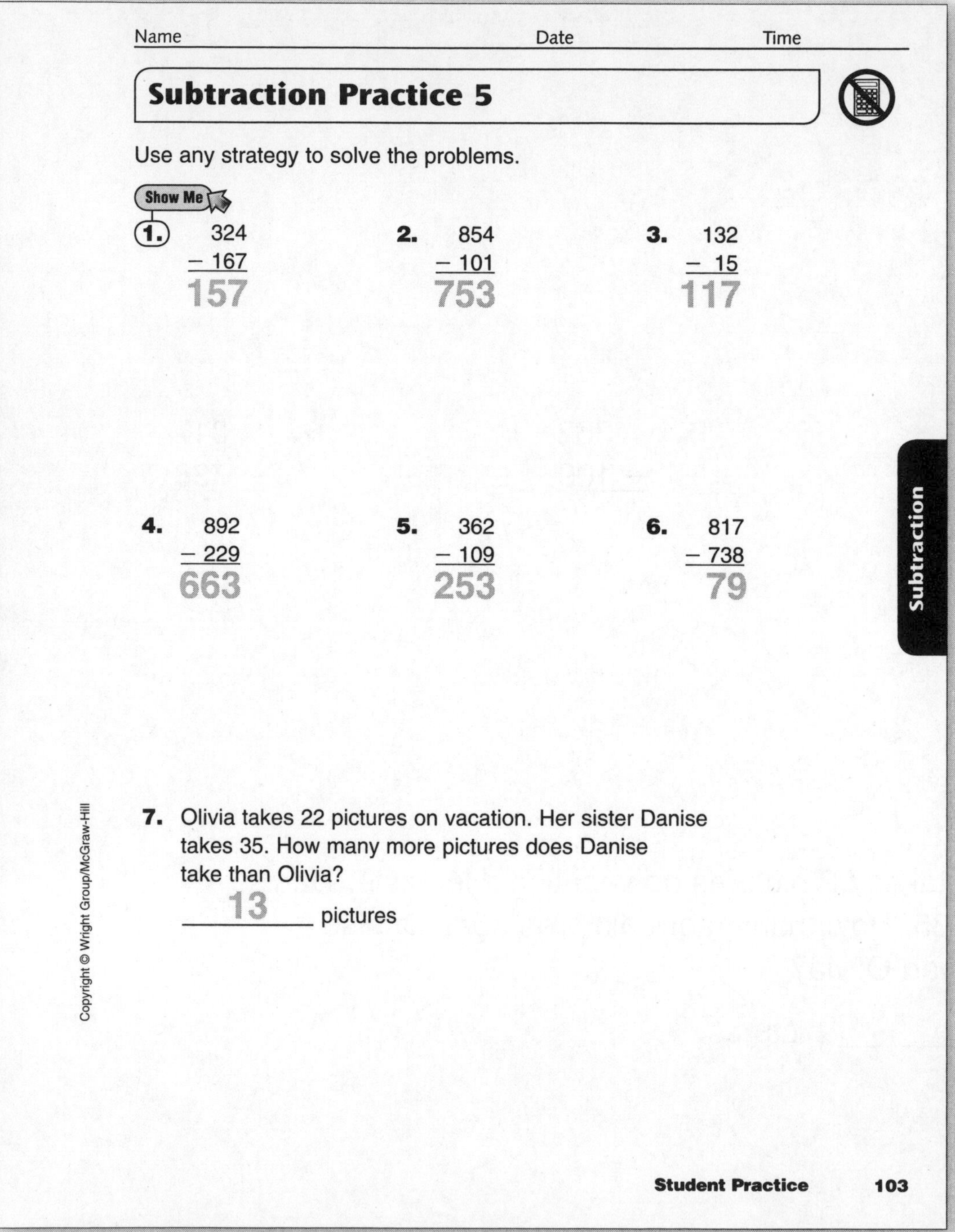

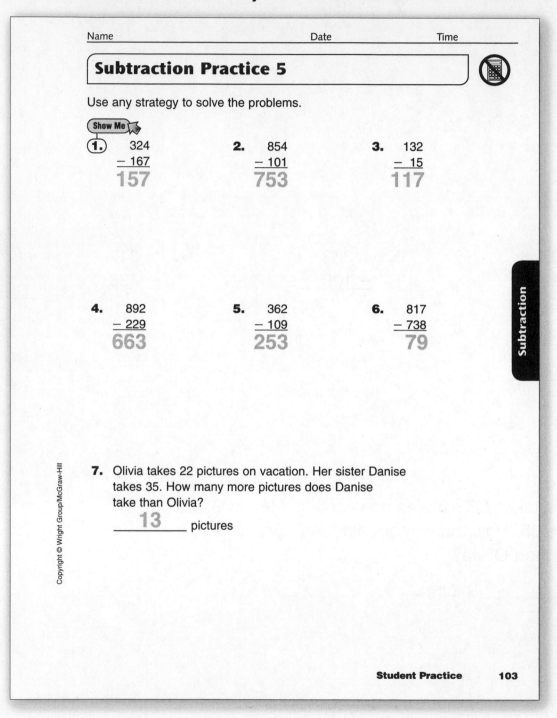

Name Date Time

Subtraction Practice 5

Use any strategy to solve the problems.

Show Me

1. 324 − 167 = **157**
2. 854 − 101 = **753**
3. 132 − 15 = **117**
4. 892 − 229 = **663**
5. 362 − 109 = **253**
6. 817 − 738 = **79**
7. Olivia takes 22 pictures on vacation. Her sister Danise takes 35. How many more pictures does Danise take than Olivia?

   13 pictures

Subtraction

Name Date Time

Addition Practice 1

Use any strategy to solve the problems.

1. 17 + 25 = ________

2. ________ = 18 + 963

3. 924 + 746 = ________

4. $\begin{array}{r} 109 \\ +\ 37 \\ \hline \end{array}$

5. $\begin{array}{r} 528 \\ +\ 12 \\ \hline \end{array}$

6. $\begin{array}{r} 522 \\ +\ 319 \\ \hline \end{array}$

7. Ms. Lewis buys 10 peaches and 12 bananas at a farm stand. How many pieces of fruit does she buy altogether?

   ________ pieces of fruit

8. Nicholas has 100 thin rubber bands. He borrows 28 thick rubber bands. How many rubber bands does he have now?

   ________ rubber bands

Answers to Addition Practice 1

While these problems may be appropriate for **third-grade** students, feel free to assign some or all of them to any student who needs practice at this level.

Recommended Use Use after Lesson 2-7 in Grade 3.

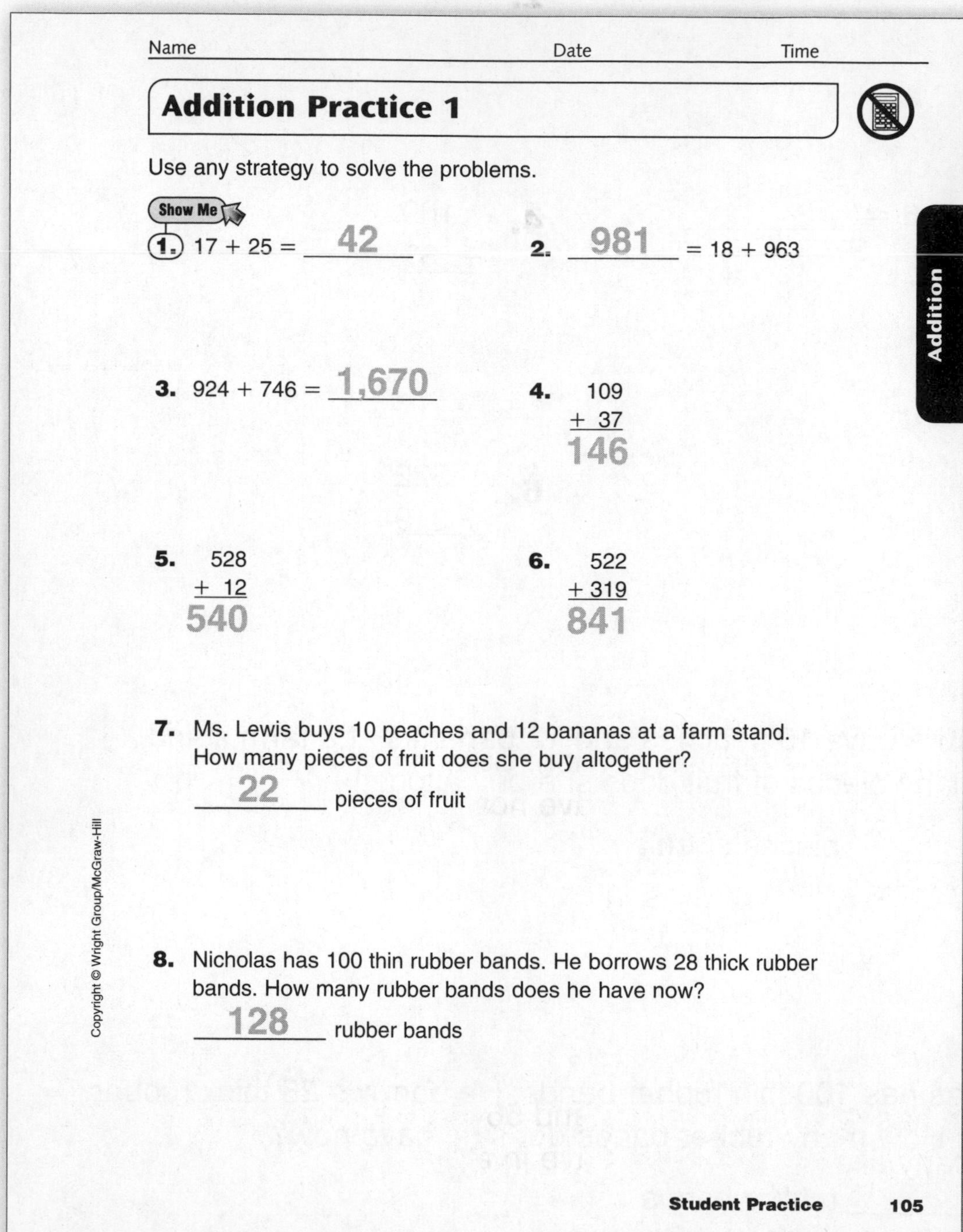

Name ____________ Date ________ Time ________

Addition Practice 1

Use any strategy to solve the problems.

Show Me

1. 17 + 25 = **42**

2. **981** = 18 + 963

3. 924 + 746 = **1,670**

4. 109 + 37 = **146**

5. 528 + 12 = **540**

6. 522 + 319 = **841**

7. Ms. Lewis buys 10 peaches and 12 bananas at a farm stand. How many pieces of fruit does she buy altogether?
   22 pieces of fruit

8. Nicholas has 100 thin rubber bands. He borrows 28 thick rubber bands. How many rubber bands does he have now?
   128 rubber bands

Addition

Student Practice 105

Name Date Time

Addition Practice 2

Use your favorite strategy to solve the following problems.

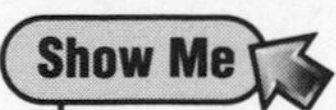

1. 248 + 187 = ______

2. ______ = 88 + 39

3. 944 + 22 = ______

4. $\begin{array}{r} 522 \\ +\ 411 \\ \hline \end{array}$

5. $\begin{array}{r} 962 \\ +\ 238 \\ \hline \end{array}$

6. $\begin{array}{r} 194 \\ +\ 132 \\ \hline \end{array}$

7. Theo has 17 rocks in his collection. Saturday, he found 21 more. How many does he have now?

   ______ rocks

8. Rashan has 42 puppy stickers and 56 kitten stickers. How many stickers does she have in all?

   ______ stickers

Addition

Answers to Addition Practice 2

While these problems may be appropriate for **third-grade** students, feel free to assign some or all of them to any student who needs practice at this level.

Recommended Use Use after Lesson 2-7 in Grade 3.

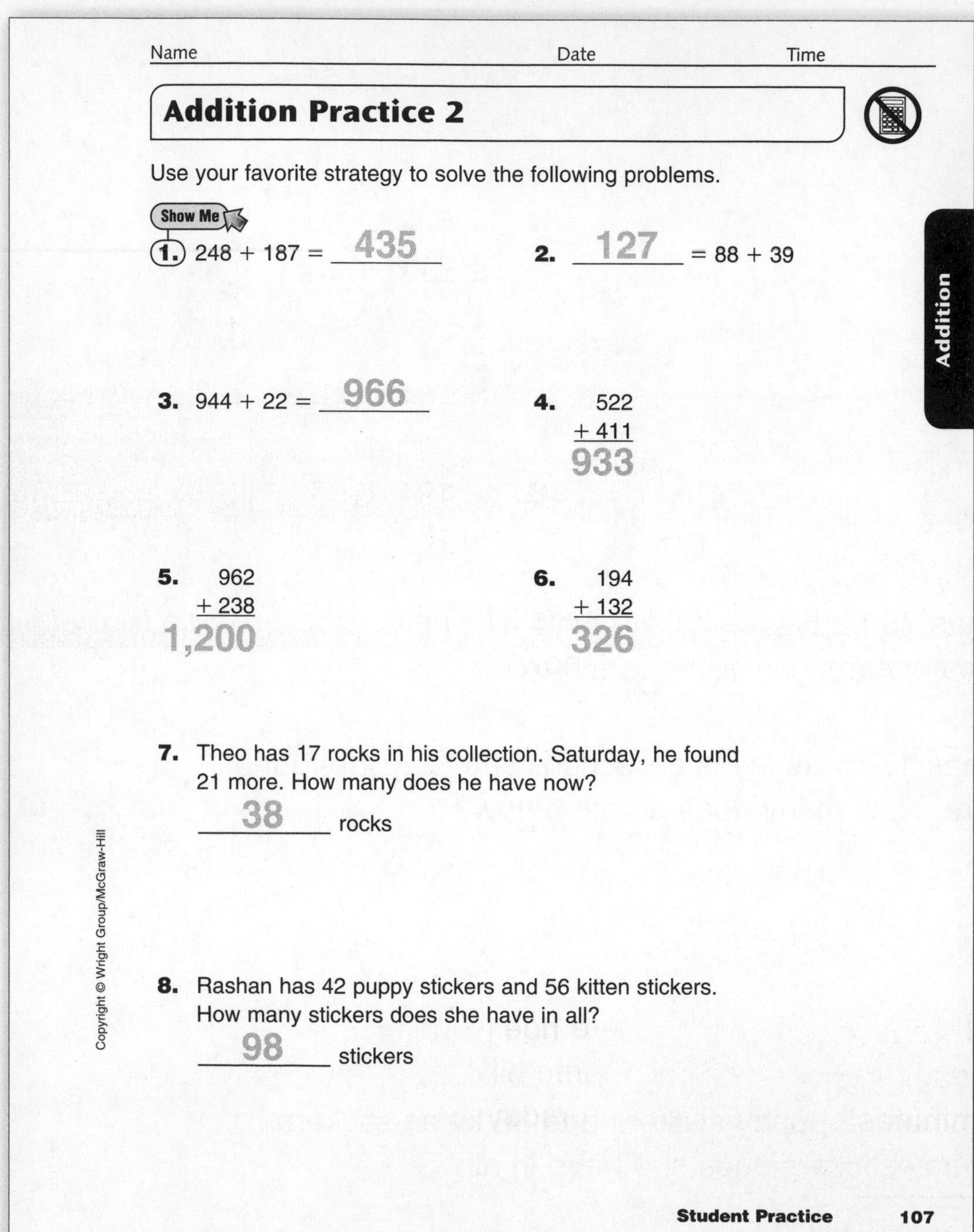

Name Date Time

Addition Practice 2

Use your favorite strategy to solve the following problems.

Show Me

1. 248 + 187 = 435
2. 127 = 88 + 39
3. 944 + 22 = 966
4. 522 + 411 = 933
5. 962 + 238 = 1,200
6. 194 + 132 = 326
7. Theo has 17 rocks in his collection. Saturday, he found 21 more. How many does he have now?
   38 rocks
8. Rashan has 42 puppy stickers and 56 kitten stickers. How many stickers does she have in all?
   98 stickers

Student Practice 107

Name Date Time

Subtraction Practice 1

Use your favorite strategy to solve the following problems.

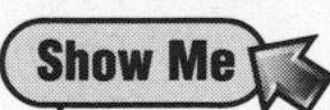

1. 60 − 27 = ______   2. ______ = 20 − 10   3. 50 − 44 = ______

4. $\begin{array}{r} 92 \\ -\ 42 \\ \hline \end{array}$ 5. $\begin{array}{r} 54 \\ -\ 11 \\ \hline \end{array}$ 6. $\begin{array}{r} 300 \\ -\ 150 \\ \hline \end{array}$

Subtraction

7. Sam has 75 trading cards. He sells 21 of them. How many cards does he have now?

   __________ trading cards

8. Miguel went on a 45 minute bike ride on Thursday. On Friday, he went on a 30 minute bike ride. How many more minutes did he ride on Thursday than on Friday?

   __________ minutes

Answers to Subtraction Practice 1

While these problems may be appropriate for **third-grade** students, feel free to assign some or all of them to any student who needs practice at this level.

Recommended Use Use after Lesson 2-8 in Grade 3.

Subtraction

Name ______ Date ______ Time ______

Subtraction Practice 1

Use your favorite strategy to solve the following problems.

Show Me

1. 60 − 27 = 33

2. 10 = 20 − 10

3. 50 − 44 = 6

4. 92 − 42 = 50

5. 54 − 11 = 43

6. 300 − 150 = 150

Subtraction

7. Sam has 75 trading cards. He sells 21 of them. How many cards does he have now?

54 trading cards

8. Miguel went on a 45 minute bike ride on Thursday. On Friday, he went on a 30 minute bike ride. How many more minutes did he ride on Thursday than on Friday?

15 minutes

Name ______________________ Date ______________ Time ______________

Subtraction Practice 2

Use your favorite strategy to solve the following problems.

1. ________ = 324 − 167

2. 603 − 204 = ________

3. 562 − 272 = ________

4. 644 − 82

5. 843 − 66

6. 670 − 424

7. Thomas finished a video game with 450 points. Caden finished with 274 points. How many more points does Thomas have?

   ________ points

8. Isabel has 109 marbles. She takes 80 marbles to school for a project. How many does she have left?

   ________ marbles

Subtraction

Answers to Subtraction Practice 2

While these problems may be appropriate for **third-grade** students, feel free to assign some or all of them to any student who needs practice at this level.

Recommended Use Use after Lesson 2-8 in Grade 3.

Name ______________________ Date ____________ Time ____________

Subtraction Practice 2

Use your favorite strategy to solve the following problems.

Show Me

1. 157 = 324 − 167

2. 603 − 204 = 399

3. 562 − 272 = 290

4. 644 − 82 = 562

5. 843 − 66 = 777

6. 670 − 424 = 246

7. Thomas finished a video game with 450 points. Caden finished with 274 points. How many more points does Thomas have?

   176 points

8. Isabel has 109 marbles. She takes 80 marbles to school for a project. How many does she have left?

   29 marbles

Subtraction

Name Date Time

Addition and Subtraction Practice 1

Use your favorite strategy to solve the following problems.

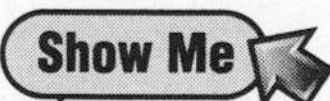

1. 325 − 38 = ______ 2. ______ = 82 − 79 3. 80 − 33 = ______

4. $\begin{array}{r} 98 \\ +\ 23 \\ \hline \end{array}$

5. $\begin{array}{r} 996 \\ +\ 371 \\ \hline \end{array}$

6. $\begin{array}{r} 86 \\ -\ 60 \\ \hline \end{array}$

7. Hannah buys a bag of 200 water balloons. She has 43 more at home. How many water balloons does she have altogether?

   ____________ water balloons

8. Millie's mother has 22 juice boxes. She gives 7 to Millie and her friends. How many juice boxes are left?

   ____________ juice boxes

Addition

Subtraction

Answers to Addition and Subtraction Practice 1

While these problems may be appropriate for **third-grade** students, feel free to assign some or all of them to any student who needs practice at this level.

Recommended Use Use after Lesson 2-8 in Grade 3.

Addition

Subtraction

Name Date Time

Addition and Subtraction Practice 1

Use your favorite strategy to solve the following problems.

Show Me

1. 325 − 38 = 287 2. 3 = 82 − 79 3. 80 − 33 = 47

4. 98 + 23 = 121

5. 996 + 371 = 1,367

6. 86 − 60 = 26

7. Hannah buys a bag of 200 water balloons. She has 43 more at home. How many water balloons does she have altogether?

243 water balloons

8. Millie's mother has 22 juice boxes. She gives 7 to Millie and her friends. How many juice boxes are left?

15 juice boxes

Addition

Subtraction

Student Practice 113

Name Date Time

Addition and Subtraction Practice 2

Use your favorite strategy to solve the following problems.

Show Me

1. 932 − 356 = __________

2. __________ = 230 + 83

3. 41 + 88 = __________

4. $\begin{array}{r} 138 \\ -\ 92 \\ \hline \end{array}$

5. $\begin{array}{r} 180 \\ +\ 69 \\ \hline \end{array}$

6. $\begin{array}{r} 425 \\ -\ 71 \\ \hline \end{array}$

7. Tamara has 23 barrettes. She gives 12 of them to her sister. How many barrettes does she have now?

__________ barrettes

8. Steven has 32 baseball and basketball trading cards. He has 15 baseball cards. How many basketball cards does he have?

__________ basketball cards

Addition

Subtraction

Answers to Addition and Subtraction Practice 2

While these problems may be appropriate for **third-grade** students, feel free to assign some or all of them to any student who needs practice at this level.

Recommended Use Use after Lesson 2-8 in Grade 3.

Name Date Time

Addition and Subtraction Practice 2

Use your favorite strategy to solve the following problems.

Show Me

1. 932 − 356 = 576

2. 313 = 230 + 83

3. 41 + 88 = 129

4. 138 − 92 = 46

5. 180 + 69 = 249

6. 425 − 71 = 354

7. Tamara has 23 barrettes. She gives 12 of them to her sister. How many barrettes does she have now?
   11 barrettes

8. Steven has 32 baseball and basketball trading cards. He has 15 baseball cards. How many basketball cards does he have?
   17 basketball cards

Name Date Time

Addition and Subtraction Practice 3

Use your favorite strategy to solve the following problems.

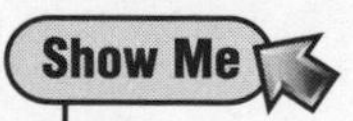

1. ______ = 80 − 27
2. 45 + 22 = ______
3. ______ = 39 + 13

4. $\begin{array}{r} 97 \\ -\ 19 \\ \hline \end{array}$

5. $\begin{array}{r} 51 \\ -\ 45 \\ \hline \end{array}$

6. $\begin{array}{r} 49 \\ +\ 13 \\ \hline \end{array}$

Addition

Subtraction

7. Harper has 21 books. For his birthday, he gets 13 more. How many books does he have now?

   ____________ books

8. There are 10 children at Leticia's birthday party. Her mother cuts her birthday cake into 12 pieces. If everyone has a piece, how many pieces are left?

   ____________ pieces

Answers to Addition and Subtraction Practice 3

While these problems may be appropriate for **third-grade** students, feel free to assign some or all of them to any student who needs practice at this level.

Recommended Use Use problems after Lesson 2-8 in Grade 3.

Addition

Subtraction

Name Date Time

Addition and Subtraction Practice 3

Use your favorite strategy to solve the following problems.

Show Me

1. 53 = 80 − 27
2. 45 + 22 = 67
3. 52 = 39 + 13

4. 97 − 19 = 78
5. 51 − 45 = 6
6. 49 + 13 = 62

7. Harper has 21 books. For his birthday, he gets 13 more. How many books does he have now?

   34 books

8. There are 10 children at Leticia's birthday party. Her mother cuts her birthday cake into 12 pieces. If everyone has a piece, how many pieces are left?

   2 pieces

Addition

Subtraction

Name Date Time

Multiplication Practice 1

Use your favorite strategy to solve the following problems.

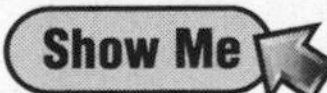

1. 5 × 26 = ______

2. ______ = 6 × 50

3. 23 × 3 = ______

4. $\begin{array}{r} 76 \\ \times\ 3 \\ \hline \end{array}$

5. $\begin{array}{r} 88 \\ \times\ 9 \\ \hline \end{array}$

6. $\begin{array}{r} 411 \\ \times\ \ \ 5 \\ \hline \end{array}$

7. In the store, there are 15 rows of oranges with 110 oranges in each row. How many oranges are in the store?

   ____________ oranges

8. Ryan bought 4 packages of peanuts at the store. Each package contained 145 peanuts. How many peanuts did Ryan have altogether?

   ____________ peanuts

Multiplication

Answers to Multiplication Practice 1

While these problems may be appropriate for **third-grade** students, feel free to assign some or all of them to any student who needs practice at this level.

Recommended Use Use after Lesson 9-4 in Grade 3.

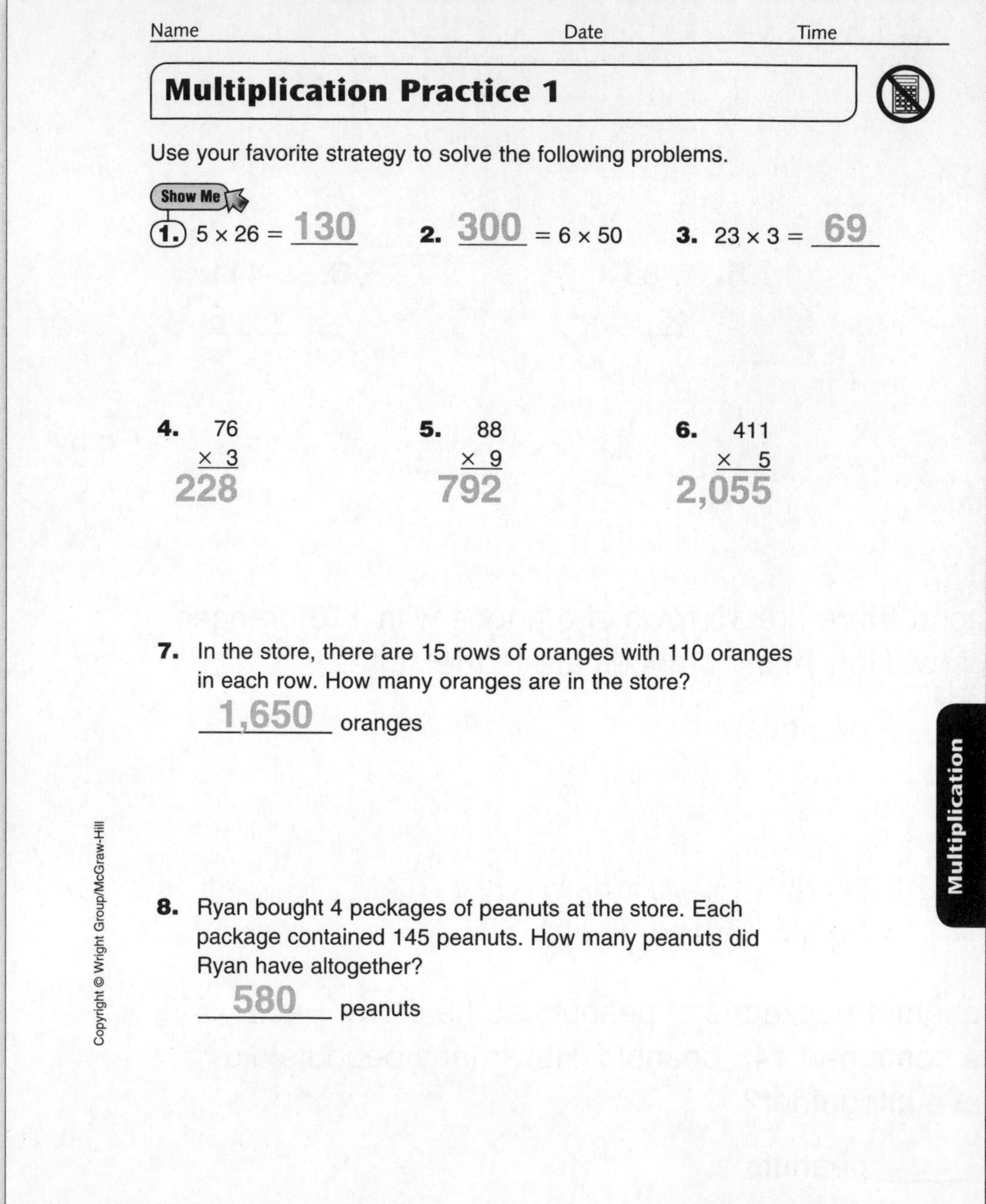

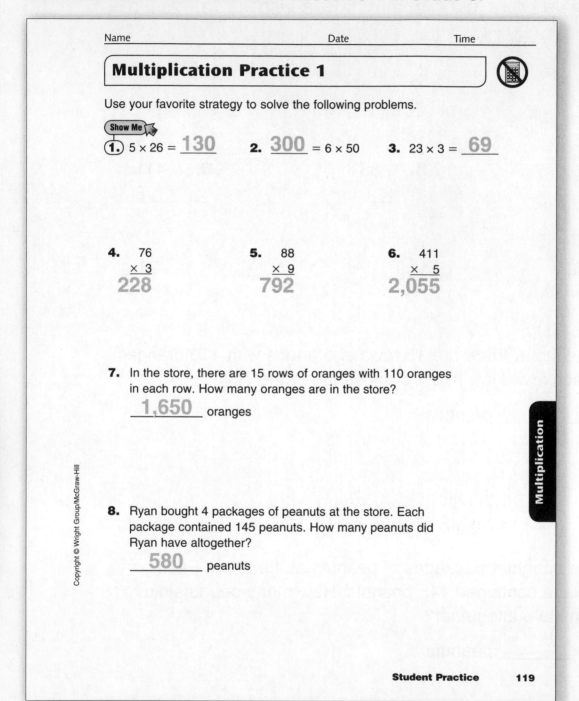

Name Date Time

Multiplication Practice 1

Use your favorite strategy to solve the following problems.

Show Me

1. 5 × 26 = 130
2. 300 = 6 × 50
3. 23 × 3 = 69

4. 76 × 3 = 228
5. 88 × 9 = 792
6. 411 × 5 = 2,055

7. In the store, there are 15 rows of oranges with 110 oranges in each row. How many oranges are in the store?

   1,650 oranges

8. Ryan bought 4 packages of peanuts at the store. Each package contained 145 peanuts. How many peanuts did Ryan have altogether?

   580 peanuts

Multiplication

Student Practice 119

Name Date Time

Multiplication Practice 2

Use your favorite strategy to solve the following problems.

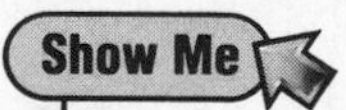

1. $7 \times \$5.93 =$ ______________

2. ______________ $= \$22.00 \times 6$

3. $\$27.00 \times 3 =$ ______________

4. $\begin{array}{r} \$1.50 \\ \times \quad 4 \\ \hline \end{array}$

5. $\begin{array}{r} \$2.25 \\ \times \quad 5 \\ \hline \end{array}$

6. $\begin{array}{r} \$7.35 \\ \times \quad 2 \\ \hline \end{array}$

7. There were 6 children at the bus stop. All of them had $1.25 for bus fare. How much money did they have altogether?

____

8. Minna bought 10 pounds of apples at $1.50 per pound. How much did she spend?

____

Multiplication

Answers to Multiplication Practice 2

While these problems may be appropriate for **third-grade** students, feel free to assign some or all of them to any student who needs practice at this level.

Recommended Use Use after Lesson 9-5 in Grade 3.

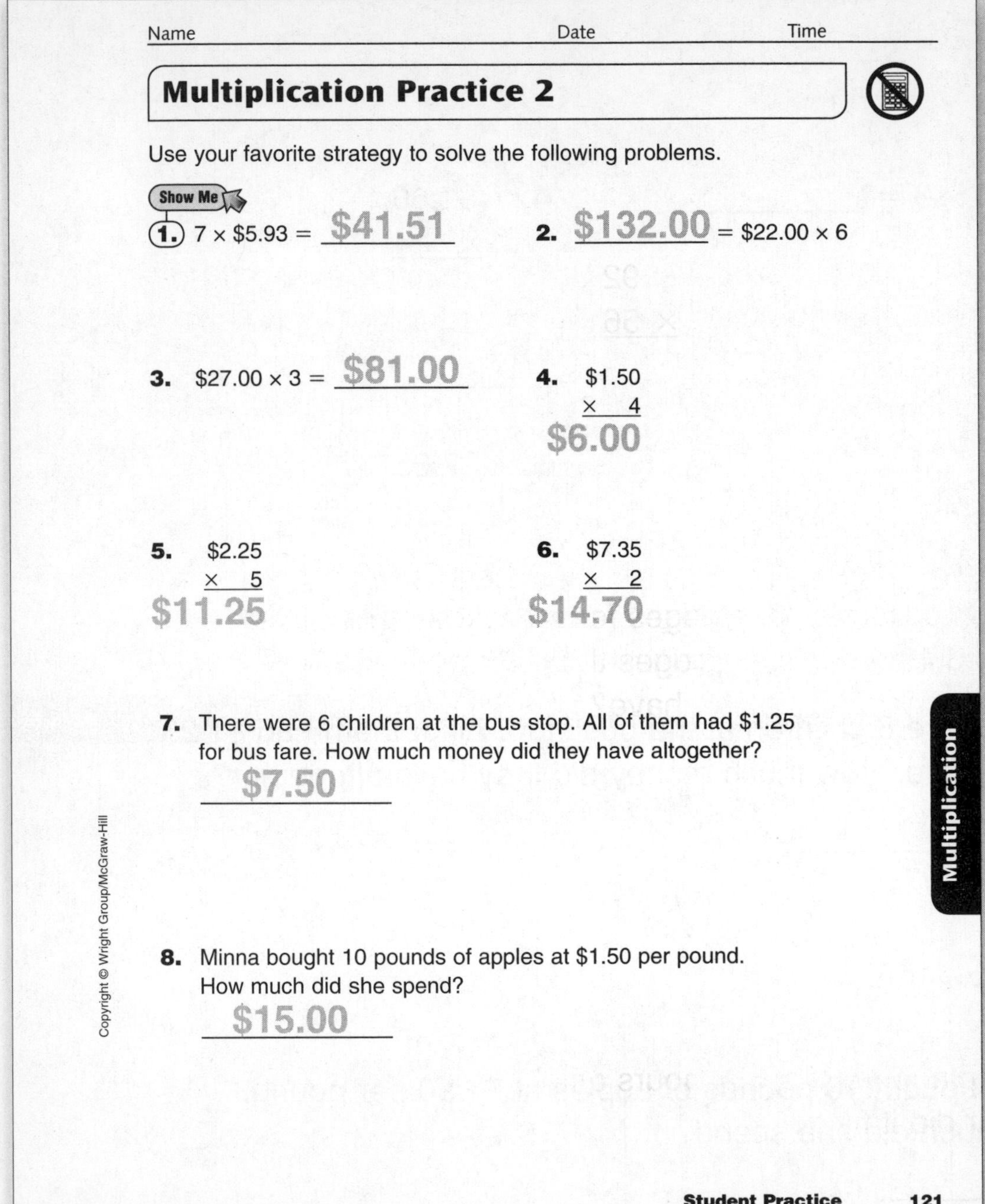

Name ______ Date ______ Time ______

Multiplication Practice 2

Use your favorite strategy to solve the following problems.

Show Me

1. 7 × $5.93 = **$41.51**

2. **$132.00** = $22.00 × 6

3. $27.00 × 3 = **$81.00**

4. $1.50 × 4 = **$6.00**

5. $2.25 × 5 = **$11.25**

6. $7.35 × 2 = **$14.70**

7. There were 6 children at the bus stop. All of them had $1.25 for bus fare. How much money did they have altogether?
$7.50

8. Minna bought 10 pounds of apples at $1.50 per pound. How much did she spend?
$15.00

Multiplication

Student Practice 121

Multiplication

Name Date Time

Multiplication Practice 3

Use your favorite strategy to solve the following problems.

1. 7 × 89 = ______

2. ______ = 4 × 40

3. ______ = 70 × 3

4. 29 × 33

5. 92 × 56

6. 106 × 12

7. Madison collected 13 pledges for the walk-a-thon. Brian collected 10 times the pledges that Madison did. How many pledges does Brian have?

 ____________ pledges

8. The airplane traveled 11 hours at 500 miles per hour. How far did it fly?

 ____________ miles

Multiplication

Answers to Multiplication Practice 3

While these problems may be appropriate for **third-grade** students, feel free to assign some or all of them to any student who needs practice at this level.

Recommended Use Use after Lesson 9-12 in Grade 3.

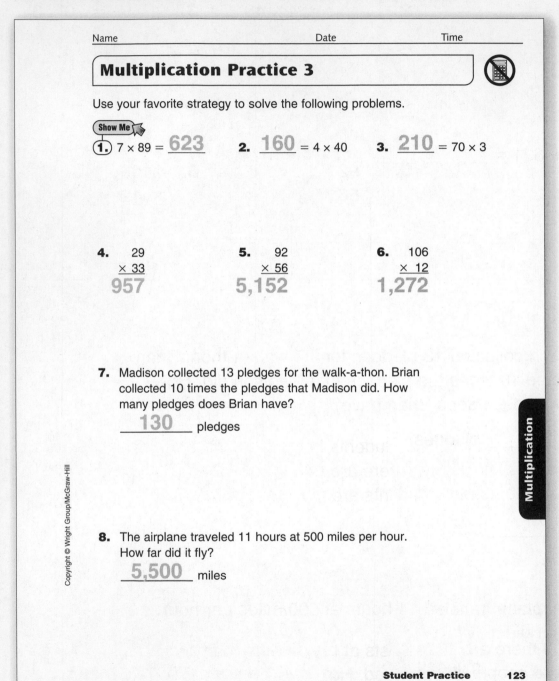

Name ______ Date ______ Time ______

Multiplication Practice 3

Use your favorite strategy to solve the following problems.

Show Me

1. 7 × 89 = 623

2. 160 = 4 × 40

3. 210 = 70 × 3

4. 29 × 33 = 957

5. 92 × 56 = 5,152

6. 106 × 12 = 1,272

7. Madison collected 13 pledges for the walk-a-thon. Brian collected 10 times the pledges that Madison did. How many pledges does Brian have?

   130 pledges

8. The airplane traveled 11 hours at 500 miles per hour. How far did it fly?

   5,500 miles

Multiplication

Student Practice 123

Multiplication

Name Date Time

Addition Practice 1

Use any strategy to solve the problems.

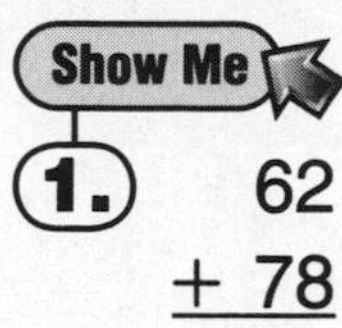

1. $\begin{array}{r} 62 \\ +\ 78 \\ \hline \end{array}$

2. ________ = 758 + 32

3. 139 + 621 = ________

4. $\begin{array}{r} 2{,}849 \\ +\ 5{,}622 \\ \hline \end{array}$

5. $\begin{array}{r} 298 \\ +\ 192 \\ \hline \end{array}$

6. ________ = 7,105 + 1,841

7. There are a total of 195 students in the 2nd and 3rd grade classes at Oak Valley. There are 203 in the 4th and 5th grade classes. How many students are in all four grades?

   ________ students

8. At 5:00 there are 122 guests at the birthday party. By 7:00, 67 more people have arrived. How many are there at 7:00?

   ________ people

Addition

Answers to Addition Practice 1

While these problems may be appropriate for **fourth-grade** students, feel free to assign some or all of them to any student who needs practice at this level.

Recommended Use Use after Lesson 2-7 in Grade 4.

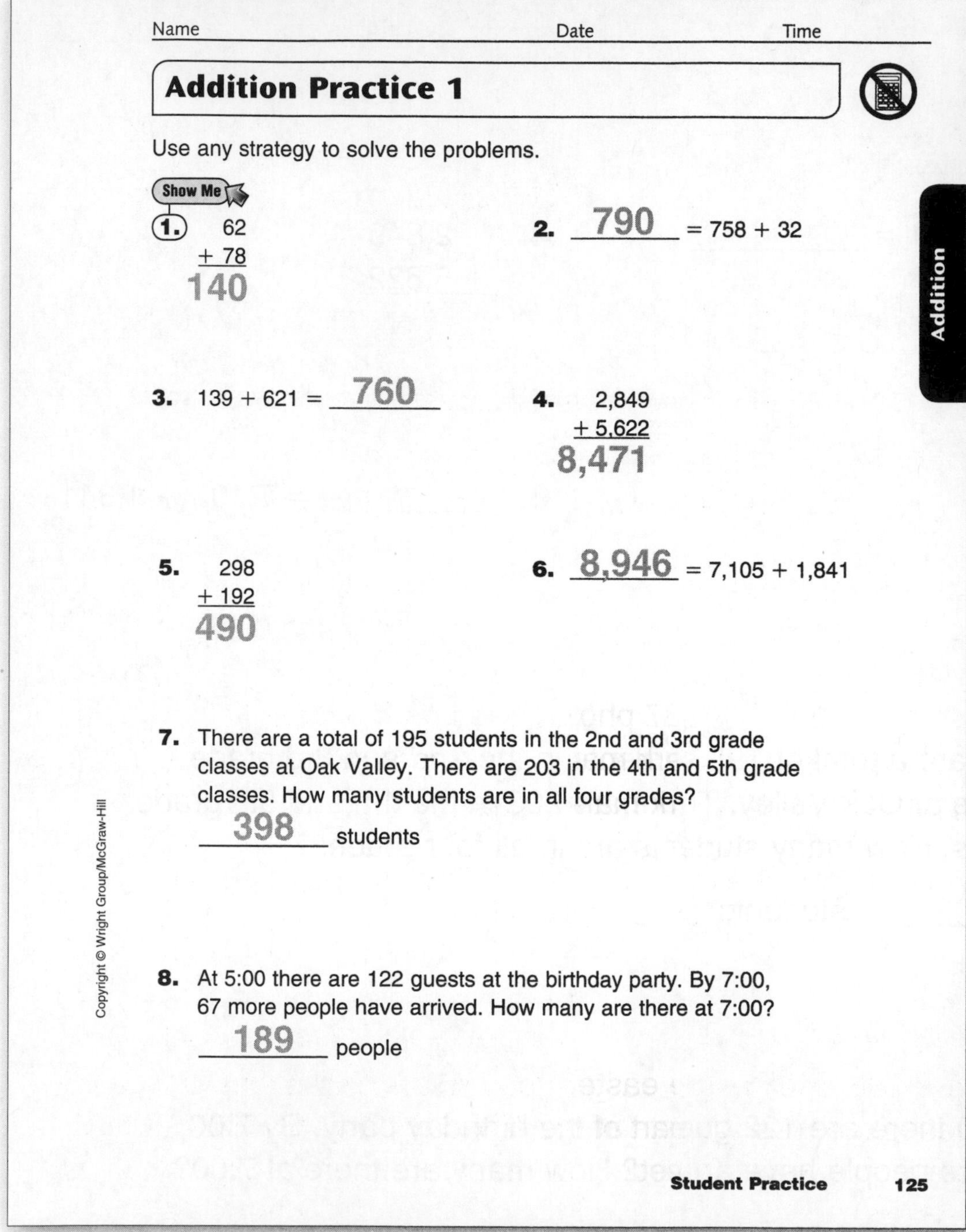

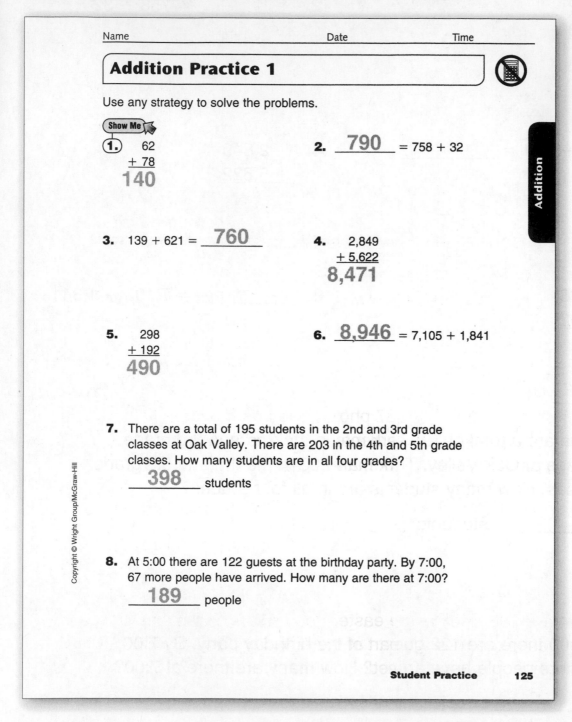

Name ____________ Date ________ Time ________

Addition Practice 1

Use any strategy to solve the problems.

Show Me

1. 62
+ 78
140

2. **790** = 758 + 32

3. 139 + 621 = **760**

4. 2,849
+ 5,622
8,471

5. 298
+ 192
490

6. **8,946** = 7,105 + 1,841

7. There are a total of 195 students in the 2nd and 3rd grade classes at Oak Valley. There are 203 in the 4th and 5th grade classes. How many students are in all four grades?
398 students

8. At 5:00 there are 122 guests at the birthday party. By 7:00, 67 more people have arrived. How many are there at 7:00?
189 people

Name Date Time

Addition Practice 2

Use any strategy to solve the problems.

1. ________ = 359 + 298

2. 1,090 + 6,212 = ________

3.
$$\begin{array}{r} 2{,}188 \\ +\ 5{,}961 \\ \hline \end{array}$$

4. ________ = 719 + 28

5.
$$\begin{array}{r} 605 \\ +\ 488 \\ \hline \end{array}$$

6.
$$\begin{array}{r} 3{,}770 \\ +\ 649 \\ \hline \end{array}$$

7. An office clerk makes 1,237 photocopies on Monday. On Tuesday, the same clerk makes 989 copies. How many copies does the clerk make in all?

__________ copies

8. There are 388 trees in the eastern part of the forest and 498 trees in the western part of the forest. How many trees are there in the whole forest?

__________ trees

Answers to Addition Practice 2

While these problems may be appropriate for **fourth-grade** students, feel free to assign some or all of them to any student who needs practice at this level.

Recommended Use Use after Lesson 2-7 in Grade 4.

Addition

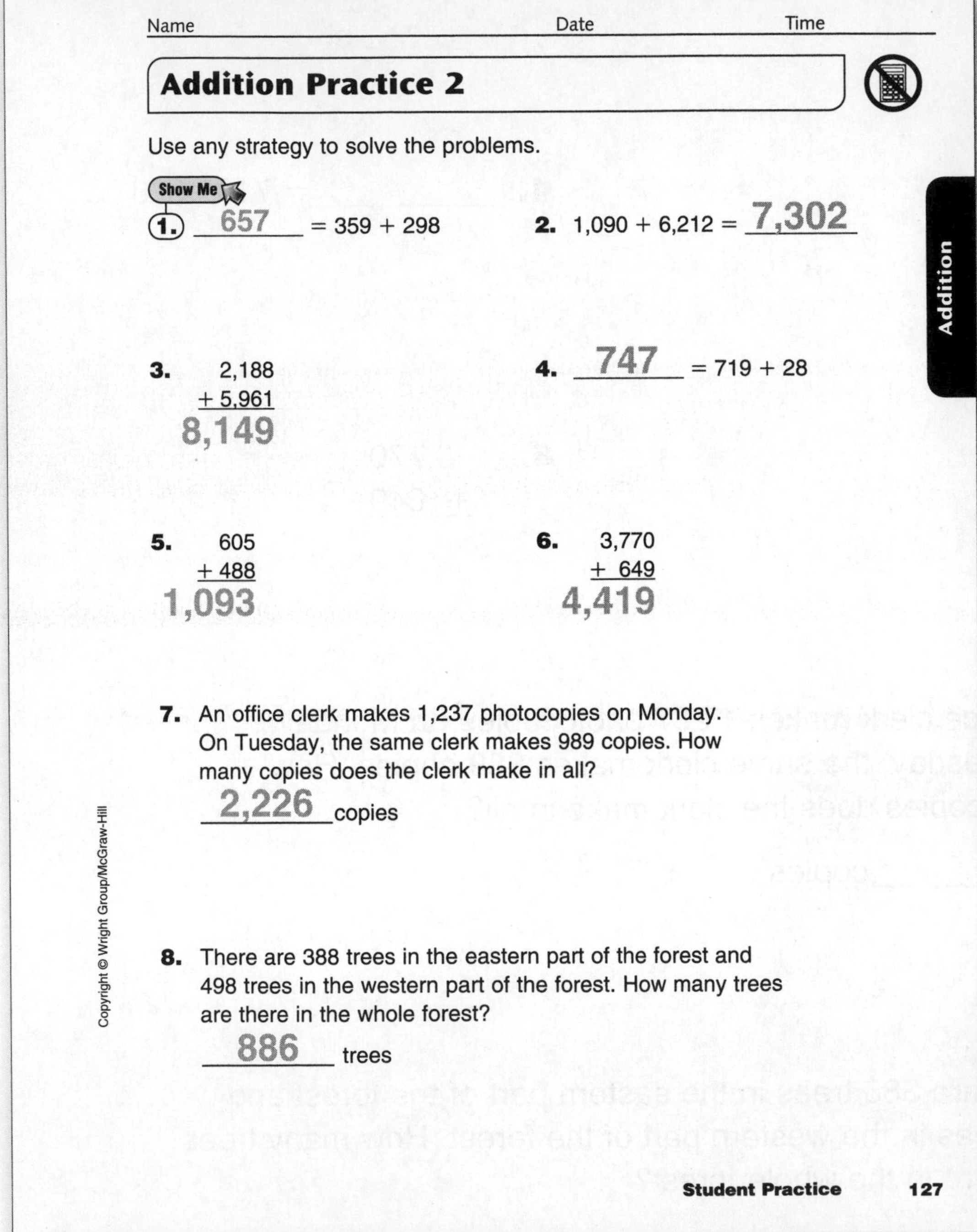

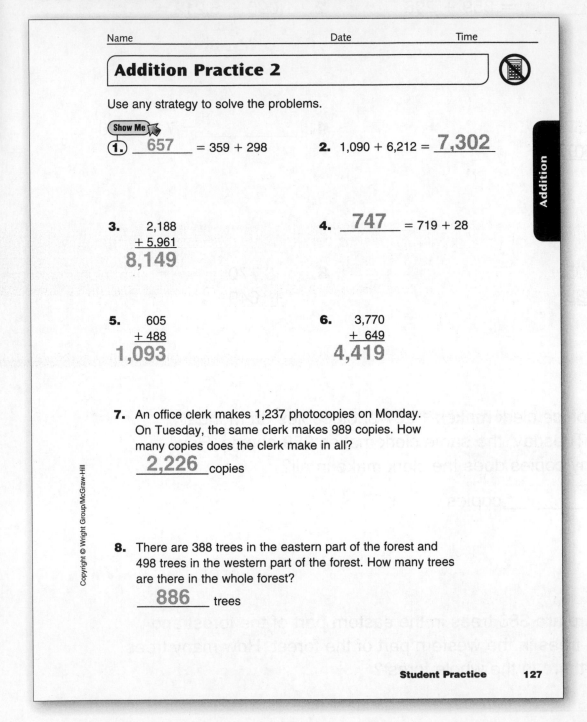

Name Date Time

Addition Practice 2

Use any strategy to solve the problems.

Show Me

1. 657 = 359 + 298

2. 1,090 + 6,212 = 7,302

3. 2,188 + 5,961 = 8,149

4. 747 = 719 + 28

5. 605 + 488 = 1,093

6. 3,770 + 649 = 4,419

7. An office clerk makes 1,237 photocopies on Monday. On Tuesday, the same clerk makes 989 copies. How many copies does the clerk make in all?

2,226 copies

8. There are 388 trees in the eastern part of the forest and 498 trees in the western part of the forest. How many trees are there in the whole forest?

886 trees

Addition

Student Practice 127

Name Date Time

Subtraction Practice 1

Use any strategy to solve the problems.

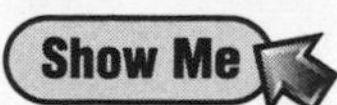

1. 352 − 164 = __________

2. __________ = 109 − 43

3. 157
− 107

4. 380 − 189 = __________

5. 500
− 92

6. 484
− 286

7. Last year, Mr. Jackson weighed 288 pounds. Over the last year, he lost 110 pounds. How much does he weigh now?

__________ pounds

8. Hilltop Farm has a total of 233 farm animals. 149 of them are cows. How many other animals are there?

__________ other animals

Subtraction

Answers to Subtraction Practice 1

While these problems may be appropriate for **fourth-grade** students, feel free to assign some or all of them to any student who needs practice at this level.

Recommended Use Use after Lesson 2-9 in Grade 4.

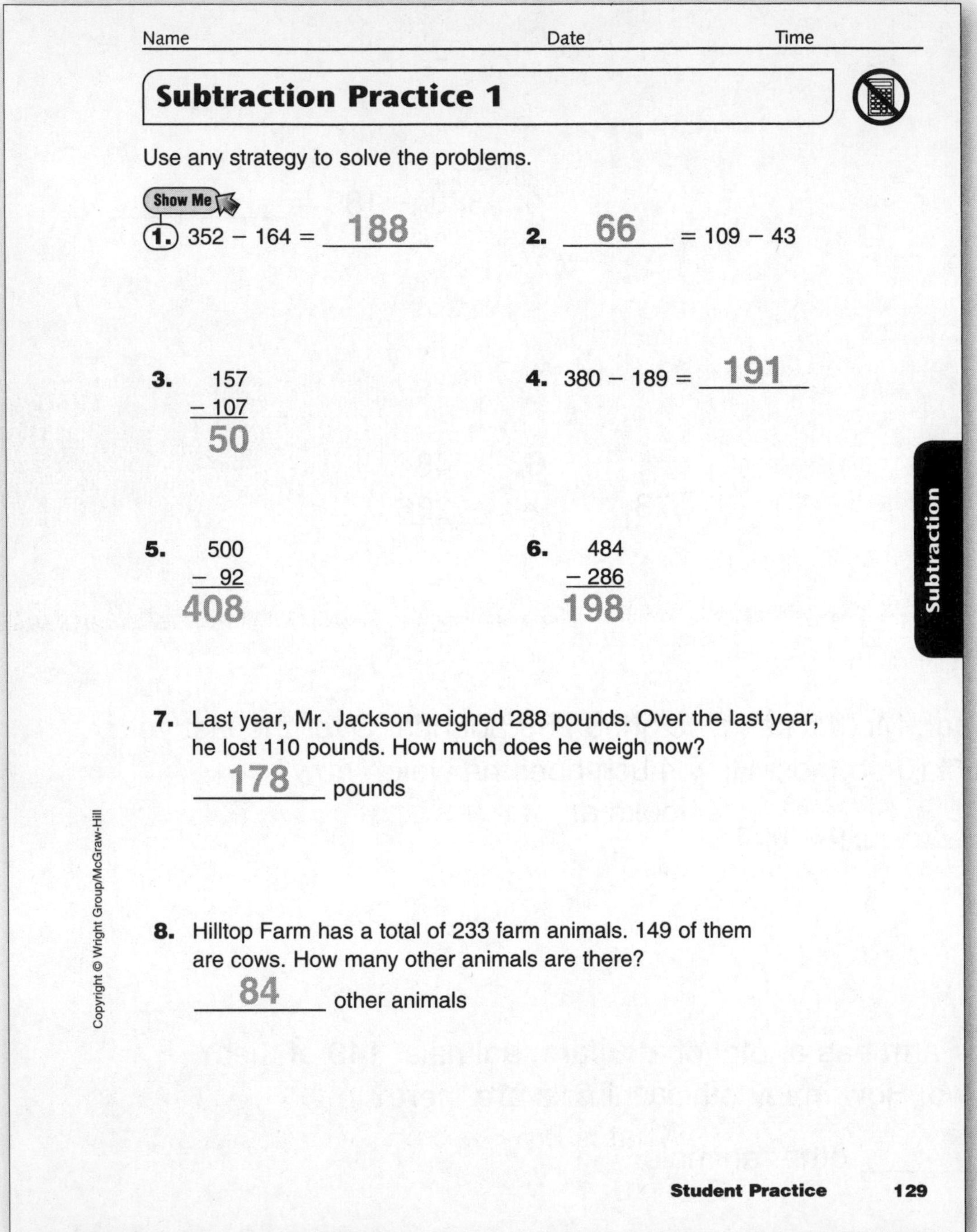
Name Date Time

Subtraction Practice 1

Use any strategy to solve the problems.

Show Me

1. 352 − 164 = 188

2. 66 = 109 − 43

3. 157 − 107 = 50

4. 380 − 189 = 191

5. 500 − 92 = 408

6. 484 − 286 = 198

7. Last year, Mr. Jackson weighed 288 pounds. Over the last year, he lost 110 pounds. How much does he weigh now?
178 pounds

8. Hilltop Farm has a total of 233 farm animals. 149 of them are cows. How many other animals are there?
84 other animals

Subtraction

Student Practice 129

Subtraction

Name Date Time

Subtraction Practice 2

Use any strategy to solve the problems.

Show Me

1. 802 − 273 = __________

2. 180
   − 166

3. __________ = 420 − 84

4. 482
   − 97

5. __________ = 5,001 − 1,378

6. 4,635
   − 2,746

7. The school library has 1,341 history books and 959 science books. How many more history books are there than science books?

   __________ books

8. Alicia writes a paper that has 1,670 words. After editing the paper, she removes 233 words. What is the word count of her paper now?

   __________ words

Answers to Subtraction Practice 2

While these problems may be appropriate for **fourth-grade** students, feel free to assign some or all of them to any student who needs practice at this level.

Recommended Use Use after Lesson 2-9 in Grade 4.

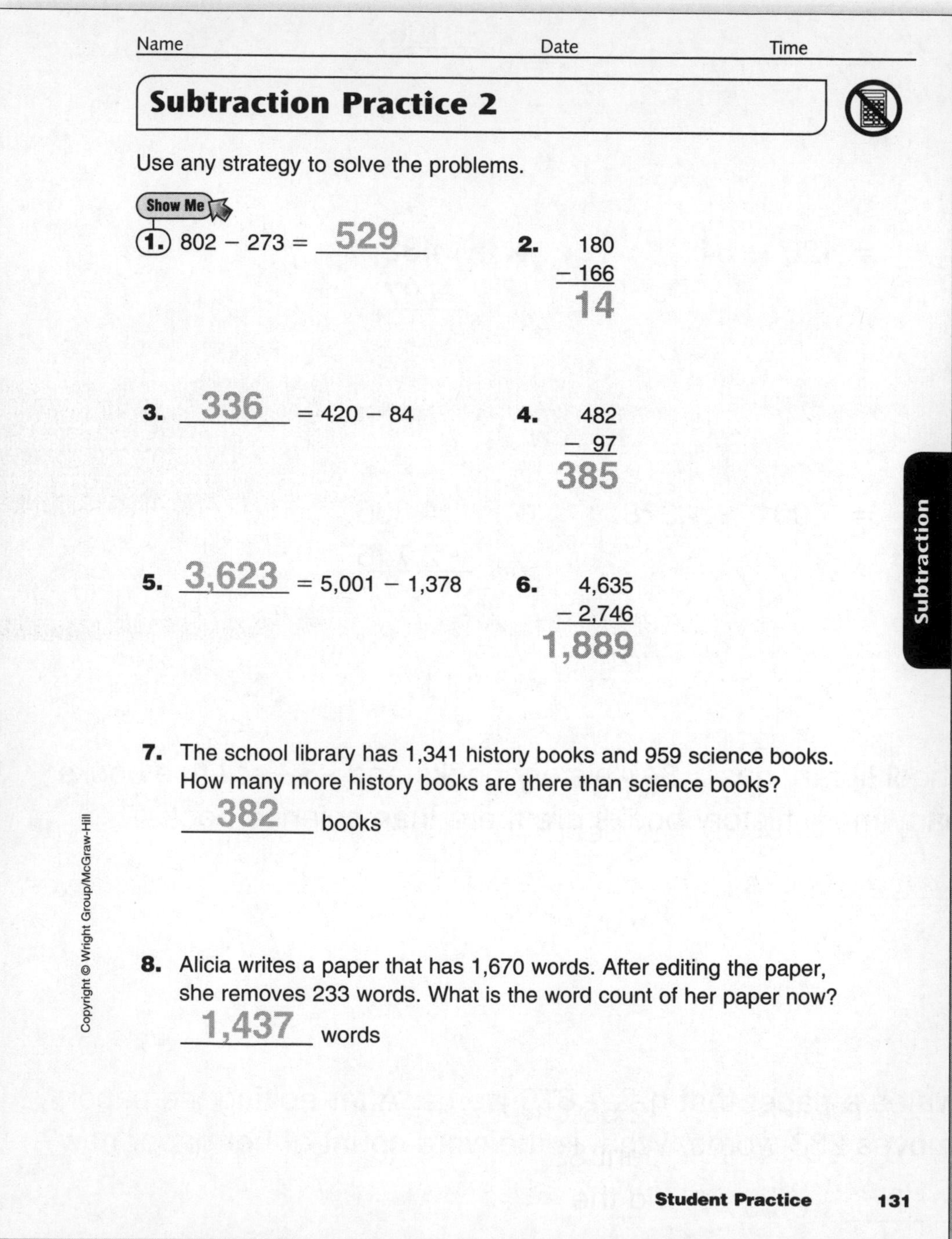

Name Date Time

Subtraction Practice 2

Use any strategy to solve the problems.

Show Me

1. 802 − 273 = 529

2. 180 − 166 = 14

3. 336 = 420 − 84

4. 482 − 97 = 385

5. 3,623 = 5,001 − 1,378

6. 4,635 − 2,746 = 1,889

7. The school library has 1,341 history books and 959 science books. How many more history books are there than science books?

   382 books

8. Alicia writes a paper that has 1,670 words. After editing the paper, she removes 233 words. What is the word count of her paper now?

   1,437 words

Subtraction

Name Date Time

Addition and Subtraction Practice

Use any strategy to solve the problems.

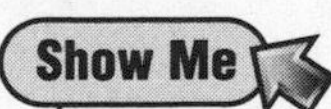

1. 8.3 − 3.75 = ________

2. ________ = 1.15 + 3.15

3. $\begin{array}{r} 10.44 \\ -\ 2.28 \\ \hline \end{array}$

4. $\begin{array}{r} 67.00 \\ -\ 63.95 \\ \hline \end{array}$

5. $\begin{array}{r} 9.68 \\ +\ 17.33 \\ \hline \end{array}$

6. 31.89 + 72.4 = ________

7. In January, Alice spent $376.23 on her family groceries. In February, she spent $401.67. How much was her grocery bill for January and February altogether?

____

8. The Ortiz family spent $342.55 on gasoline for the month of June. The Fox family spent $259.87 on gasoline for the same period. How much more did the Ortiz family spend?

____

Addition

Subtraction

Answers to Addition and Subtraction Practice

While these problems may be appropriate for **fourth-grade** students, feel free to assign some or all of them to any student who needs practice at this level.

Recommended Use Use any time after Lesson 4-5 in Grade 4.

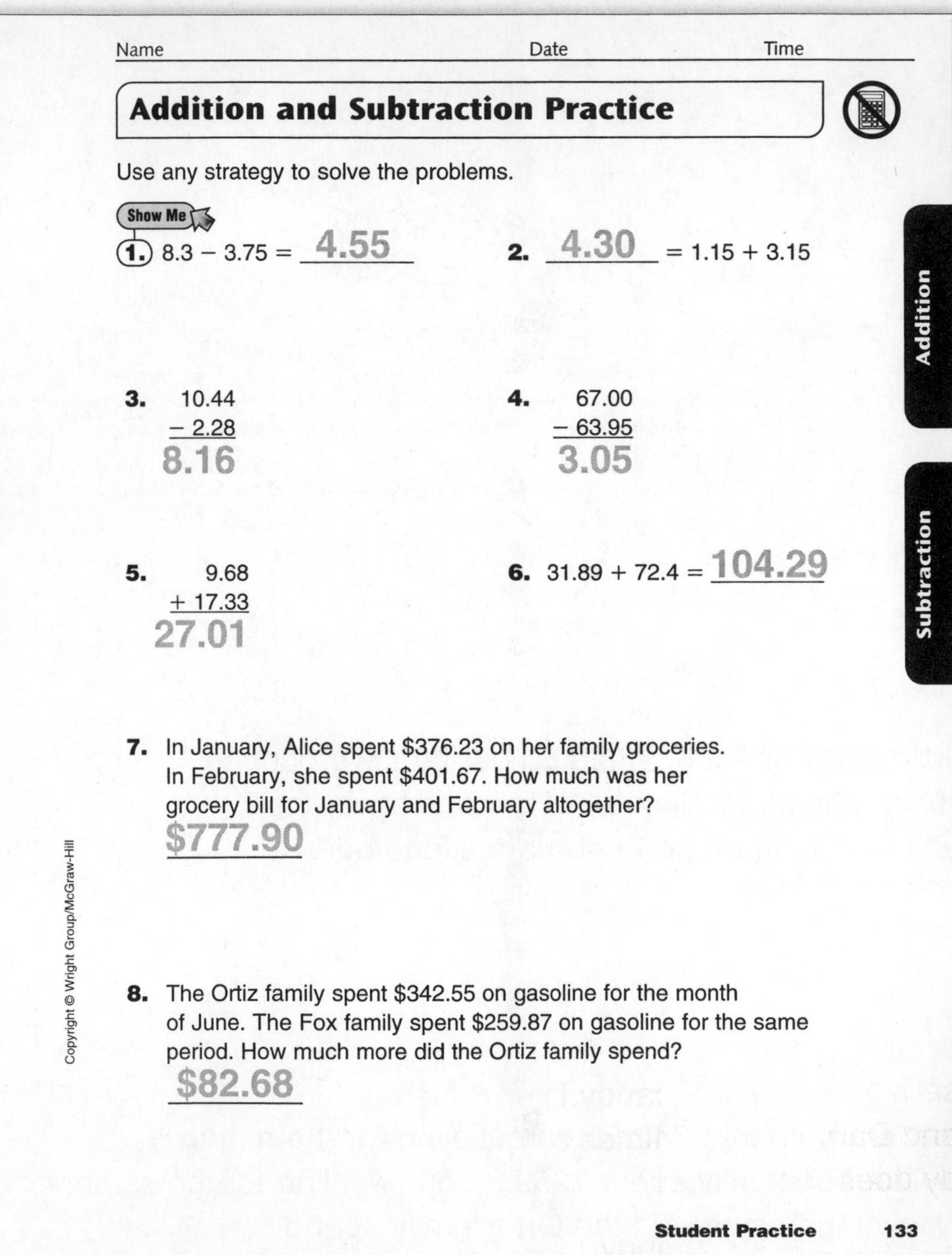

Name Date Time

Addition and Subtraction Practice

Use any strategy to solve the problems.

Show Me

1. 8.3 − 3.75 = 4.55

2. 4.30 = 1.15 + 3.15

3. 10.44 − 2.28 = 8.16

4. 67.00 − 63.95 = 3.05

5. 9.68 + 17.33 = 27.01

6. 31.89 + 72.4 = 104.29

7. In January, Alice spent $376.23 on her family groceries. In February, she spent $401.67. How much was her grocery bill for January and February altogether? $777.90

8. The Ortiz family spent $342.55 on gasoline for the month of June. The Fox family spent $259.87 on gasoline for the same period. How much more did the Ortiz family spend? $82.68

Student Practice 133

Addition

Subtraction

Name Date Time

Multiplication Practice 1

Use any strategy to solve the problems.

Show Me

1. ________ = 5 × 815

2. 20 × 9 = ________

3. 32
   $*$ 8

4. 76
   × 7

5. 125 $*$ 67 = ________

6. 416
   $*$ 27

7. The children's library has 32 shelves with 25 books on each shelf. How many books are in the children's library?

   ________ books

8. Tricia sells 118 boxes of candy for the school fundraiser. Her friend Damon sells 4 times as many. How many boxes of candy does Damon sell?

   ________ boxes of candy

Answers to Multiplication Practice 1

While these problems may be appropriate for **fourth-grade** students, feel free to assign some or all of them to any student who needs practice at this level.

Recommended Use Use any time after Lesson 5-6 in Grade 4.

Name ____________ Date ____________ Time ____________

Multiplication Practice 1

Use any strategy to solve the problems.

Show Me

1. 4,075 = 5 × 815

2. 20 × 9 = 180

3. 32 * 8 = 256

4. 76 × 7 = 532

5. 125 * 67 = 8,375

6. 416 * 27 = 11,232

7. The children's library has 32 shelves with 25 books on each shelf. How many books are in the children's library?

   800 books

8. Tricia sells 118 boxes of candy for the school fundraiser. Her friend Damon sells 4 times as many. How many boxes of candy does Damon sell?

   472 boxes of candy

Multiplication

Multiplication

Name Date Time

Multiplication Practice 2

Use any strategy to solve the problems.

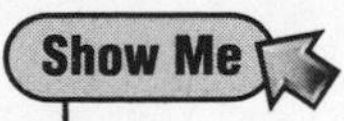

1. ________ = 3 * 45

2. 77 × 3 = ________

3. 660
   * 4

4. ________ = 694 × 4

5. 12
   * 39

6. 642 * 35 = ________

7. Mr. O'Connor gets 30 miles per gallon of gas. If Mr. O'Connor puts 12 gallons of gas in the car, how far can he go?

   ________ miles

8. The grocery story display has 15 rows of 21 cans each. How many cans are in the display?

   ________ cans

Multiplication

Answers to Multiplication Practice 2

While these problems may be appropriate for **fourth-grade** students, feel free to assign some or all of them to any student who needs practice at this level.

Recommended Use Use any time after Lesson 5-7 in Grade 4.

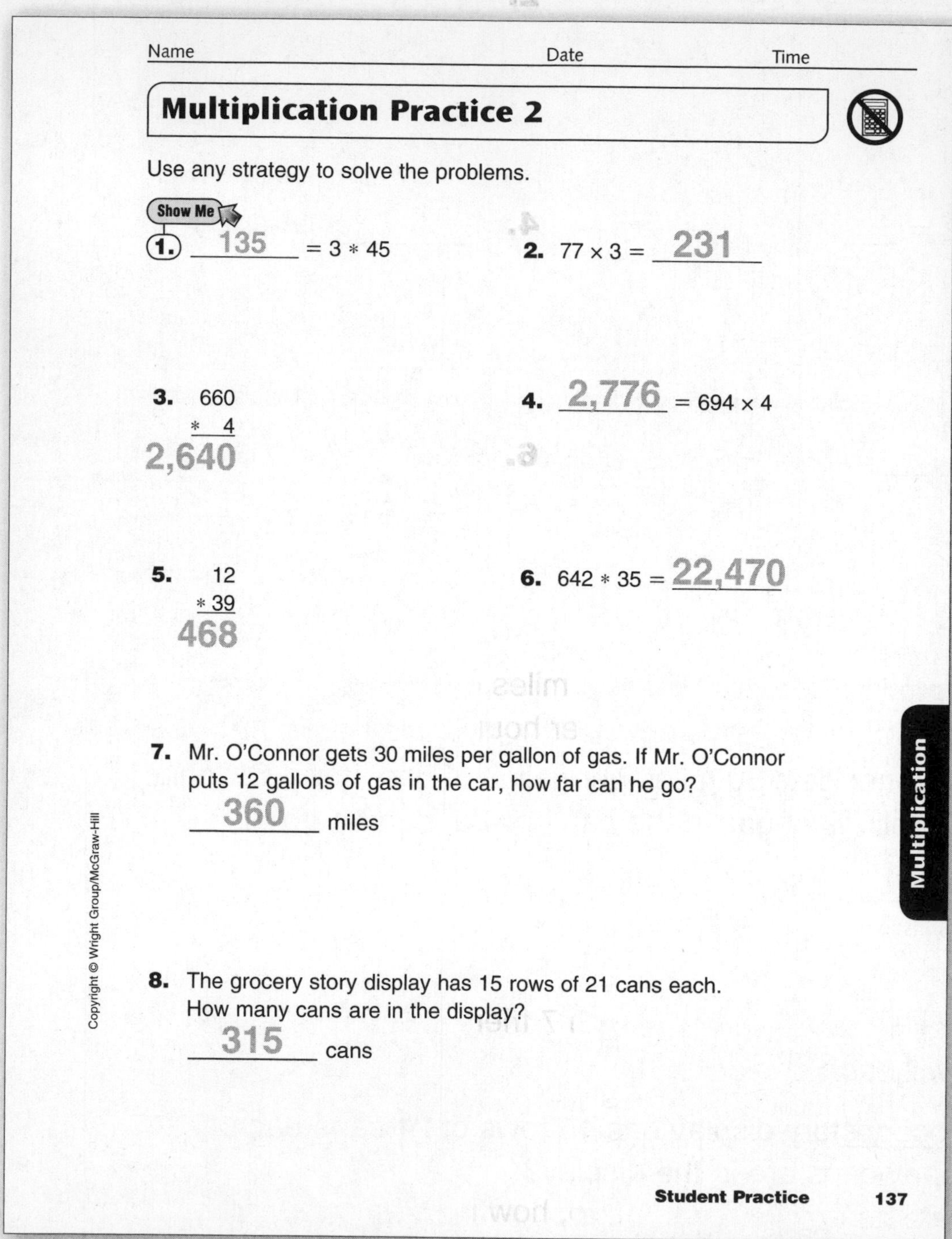
Name Date Time

Multiplication Practice 2

Use any strategy to solve the problems.

Show Me

1. 135 = 3 * 45

2. 77 × 3 = 231

3. 660 * 4 = 2,640

4. 2,776 = 694 × 4

5. 12 * 39 = 468

6. 642 * 35 = 22,470

7. Mr. O'Connor gets 30 miles per gallon of gas. If Mr. O'Connor puts 12 gallons of gas in the car, how far can he go?
360 miles

8. The grocery story display has 15 rows of 21 cans each. How many cans are in the display?
315 cans

Multiplication

Student Practice 137

Name Date Time

Division Practice 1

Use any strategy to solve the problems.

1. 94 / 6 = __________

2. __________ = 45 ÷ 9

3. 630 / 2 = __________

4. $3\overline{)214}$

5. __________ = 152 ÷ 6

6. $8\overline{)4{,}000}$

7. Jack's mother rides her bike 20 miles on Saturday. It takes her 4 hours. How many miles per hour did she travel?

   __________ miles per hour

8. Sam has 57 treats to share with 7 friends. How many treats will each person get?

   __________ treats

   Will there be any left over? If so, how many? __________

Division

Answers to Division Practice 1

While these problems may be appropriate for **fourth-grade** students, feel free to assign some or all of them to any student who needs practice at this level.

Recommended Use Use after Lesson 6-3 in Grade 4.

Name ______ Date ______ Time ______

Division Practice 1

Use any strategy to solve the problems.

Show Me

1. 94 / 6 = 15 R4
2. 5 = 45 ÷ 9
3. 630 / 2 = 315
4. 3)214 — 71 R1
5. 25 R2 = 152 ÷ 6
6. 8)4,000 — 500
7. Jack's mother rides her bike 20 miles on Saturday. It takes her 4 hours. How many miles per hour did she travel?

   5 miles per hour
8. Sam has 57 treats to share with 7 friends. How many treats will each person get?

   8 treats

   Will there be any left over? If so, how many? yes; 1

Division

Division

Name Date Time

Division Practice 2

Use any strategy to solve the problems.

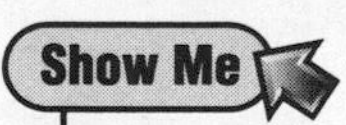

1. ________ = 758 / 28

2. 610 ÷ 54 = ________

3. 36)228

4. 881 / 22 = ________

5. 18)754

6. ________ = 1,290 ÷ 42

7. Tim's car gets 35 miles per gallon of gas. Tim plans to drive 439 miles to see his grandparents. How many gallons of gas will he need?

   ________ gallons

8. A small swimming pool holds 56 gallons of water. A larger swimming pool holds 728 gallons of water. How much more water does the larger swimming pool hold?

   ________ times more water

Answers to Division Practice 2

While these problems may be appropriate for **fourth-grade** students, feel free to assign some or all of them to any student who needs practice at this level.

Recommended Use Use after Lesson 6-10 in Grade 4.

Name ______ Date ______ Time ______

Division Practice 2

Use any strategy to solve the problems.

Show Me

1. 27 R2 = 758 / 28

2. 610 ÷ 54 = 11 R16

3. 36)228 — 6 R12

4. 881 / 22 = 40 R1

5. 18)754 — 41 R16

6. 30 R30 = 1,290 ÷ 42

7. Tim's car gets 35 miles per gallon of gas. Tim plans to drive 439 miles to see his grandparents. How many gallons of gas will he need?
   12 R19 or 13 gallons

8. A small swimming pool holds 56 gallons of water. A larger swimming pool holds 728 gallons of water. How much more water does the larger swimming pool hold?
   13 times more water

Division

Division

Name Date Time

Multiplication and Division Practice

Use any strategy to solve the problems.

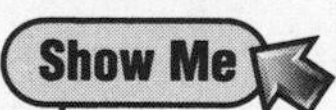

1. $7.29 * 4 = ________

2. 27.13
   * 6

3. 6.19
   * 50

4. 14.8 ÷ 4 = ________

5. 4.8
   * 4.2

6. 16)$60.80

7. At the garage sale, Teresa and her two sisters sold their trading cards for $16.08. If they divide the money equally among themselves, how much will each person get?

   ____

8. If Danesha has $15.00, how many bracelets can she buy if they're $0.75 each?

   ________ bracelets

Multiplication

Division

Answers to Multiplication and Division Practice

While these problems may be appropriate for **fourth-grade** students, feel free to assign some or all of them to any student who needs practice at this level.

Recommended Use Use any time after Lesson 9-9 Grade 4.

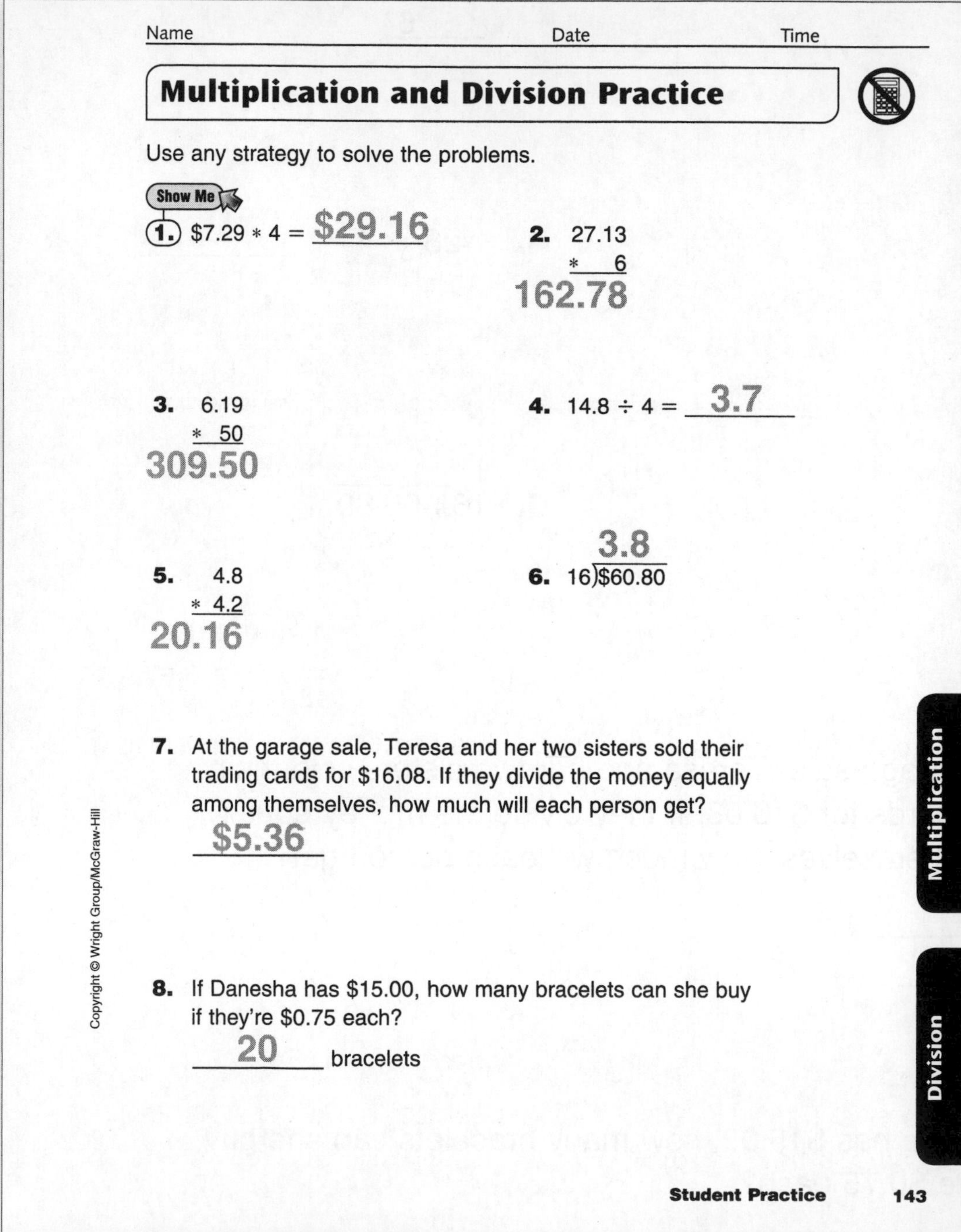

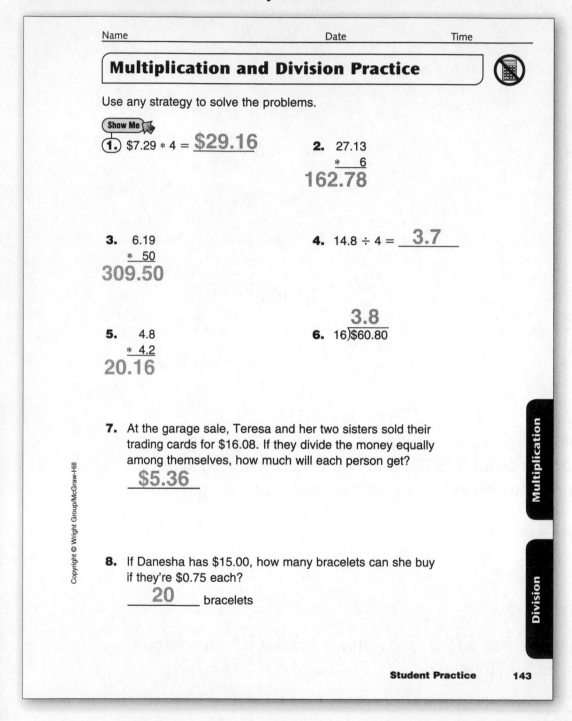

Name Date Time

Multiplication and Division Practice

Use any strategy to solve the problems.

Show Me

1. $7.29 * 4 = **$29.16**

2. 27.13 * 6 = **162.78**

3. 6.19 * 50 = **309.50**

4. 14.8 ÷ 4 = **3.7**

5. 4.8 * 4.2 = **20.16**

6. 16)$60.80 **3.8**

7. At the garage sale, Teresa and her two sisters sold their trading cards for $16.08. If they divide the money equally among themselves, how much will each person get? **$5.36**

8. If Danesha has $15.00, how many bracelets can she buy if they're $0.75 each? **20** bracelets

Multiplication

Division

Multiplication

Division

Name Date Time

Addition Practice 1

Use any strategy to solve the problems.

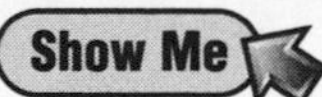

1. 348 + 177 = __________

2. __________ = 98 + 74

3. 556 + 47 = __________

4.
```
  330
  153
+ 498
```

5.
```
  3,089
+ 2,946
```

6.
```
  3,493
+ 5,629
```

7. The Johnsons fly 2,541 miles on the way to their vacation spot and 2,709 miles on the way back. How many miles do they fly in all?

____

8. Simon has 144 marbles in a jar, 206 marbles in a leather pouch, and 58 more in a tin. How many marbles does he have in his collection altogether?

____

Addition

Answers to Addition Practice 1

While these problems may be appropriate for **fifth-grade** students, feel free to assign some or all of them to any student who needs practice at this level.

Recommended Use Use any time after Lesson 2-2 in Grade 5.

Addition

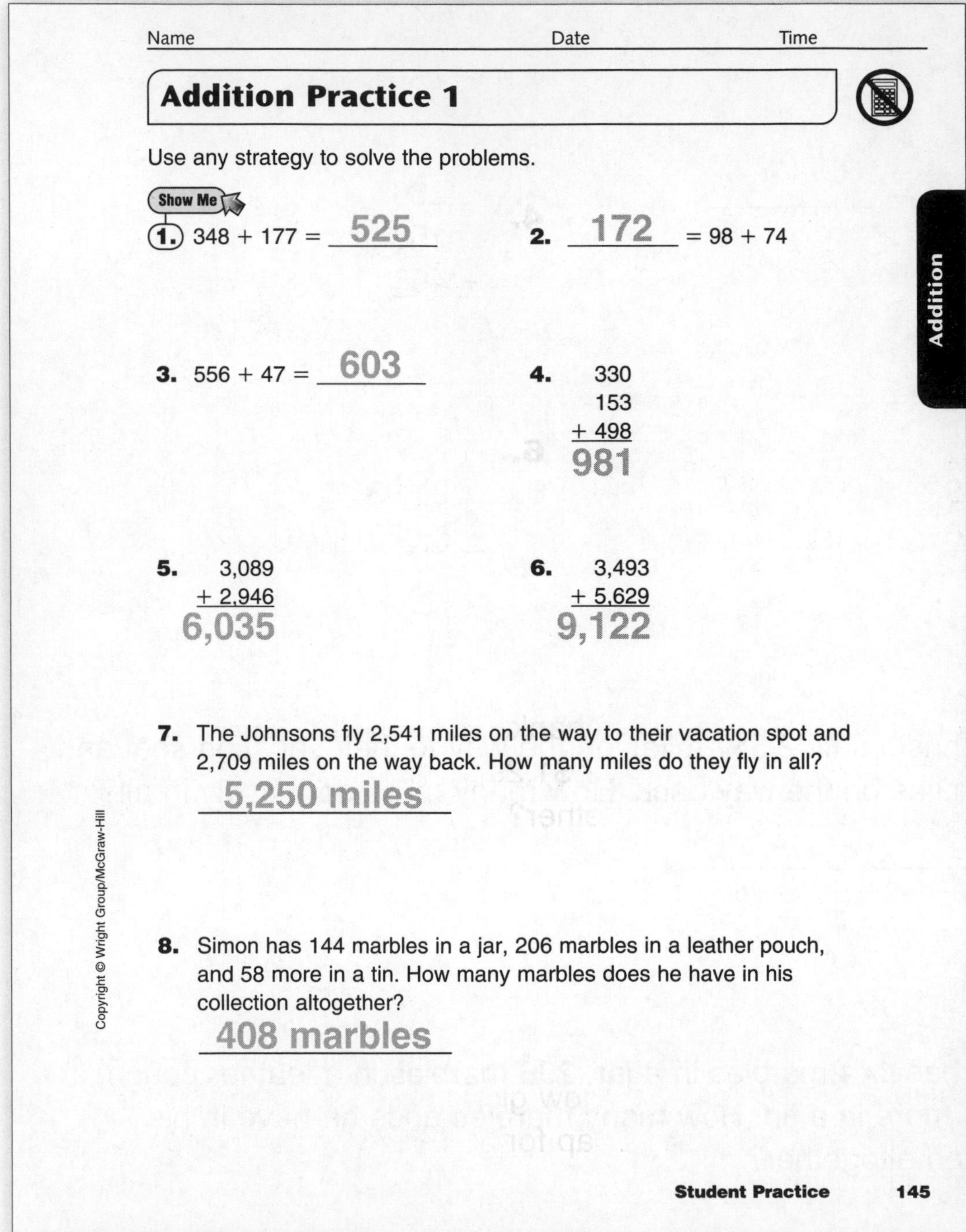

Name Date Time

Addition Practice 1

Use any strategy to solve the problems.

Show Me

1. 348 + 177 = 525

2. 172 = 98 + 74

3. 556 + 47 = 603

4. 330 + 153 + 498 = 981

5. 3,089 + 2,946 = 6,035

6. 3,493 + 5,629 = 9,122

7. The Johnsons fly 2,541 miles on the way to their vacation spot and 2,709 miles on the way back. How many miles do they fly in all?
5,250 miles

8. Simon has 144 marbles in a jar, 206 marbles in a leather pouch, and 58 more in a tin. How many marbles does he have in his collection altogether?
408 marbles

Addition

Student Practice 145

Name Date Time

Addition Practice 2

Use any strategy to solve the problems.

1. ________ = 9.87 + 2.56

2. 4.905 + 3.362 = ________

3. ________ = 1.88 + 5.176

4. ________ = 97.93 + 125

5. $\begin{array}{r} 28.9 \\ +\ 4.56 \\ \hline \end{array}$

6. $\begin{array}{r} \$10.79 \\ +\ \$23.80 \\ \hline \end{array}$

7. Ronald has $22.15 in his piggy bank. He receives $10.50 for his birthday and has another $1.29 in his pocket. How much does he have altogether?

____

8. On vacation, Sumesh buys a snow globe for $5.82, a souvenir pen for $2.97, and a baseball cap for $9.59. How much does he spend altogether?

____

Addition

Answers to Addition Practice 2

While these problems may be appropriate for **fifth-grade** students, feel free to assign some or all of them to any student who needs practice at this level.

Recommended Use Use any time after Lesson 2-2 in Grade 5.

Name ________________ Date ________ Time ________

Addition Practice 2

Use any strategy to solve the problems.

Show Me

1. 12.43 = 9.87 + 2.56

2. 4.905 + 3.362 = 8.267

3. 7.056 = 1.88 + 5.176

4. 222.93 = 97.93 + 125

5. 28.9 + 4.56 = 33.46

6. $10.79 + $23.80 = $34.59

7. Ronald has $22.15 in his piggy bank. He receives $10.50 for his birthday and has another $1.29 in his pocket. How much does he have altogether?
   $33.94

8. On vacation, Sumesh buys a snow globe for $5.82, a souvenir pen for $2.97, and a baseball cap for $9.59. How much does he spend altogether?
   $18.38

Name _______________ Date _______________ Time _______________

Subtraction Practice 1

Use any strategy to solve the problems.

Show Me

1. 846 − 363 = ____________

2. $\begin{array}{r} 392 \\ -\ 67 \\ \hline \end{array}$

3. $\begin{array}{r} 560 \\ -\ 248 \\ \hline \end{array}$

4. ____________ = 5,780 − 694

5. $\begin{array}{r} 1{,}794 \\ -\ 1{,}086 \\ \hline \end{array}$

6. ____________ = 4,006 − 1,353

7. The school band earned $1,103 from magazine subscriptions in one year. The next year, they earned $898.57. How much less money did the band earn the second year?

____

8. Shakita has $42.50. On Saturday, she spends $5.97 on lunch and $2.20 on bus fare. How much does she have left?

____

Subtraction

Answers to Subtraction Practice 1

While these problems may be appropriate for **fifth-grade** students, feel free to assign some or all of them to any student who needs practice at this level.

Recommended Use Use after Lesson 2-3 in Grade 5.

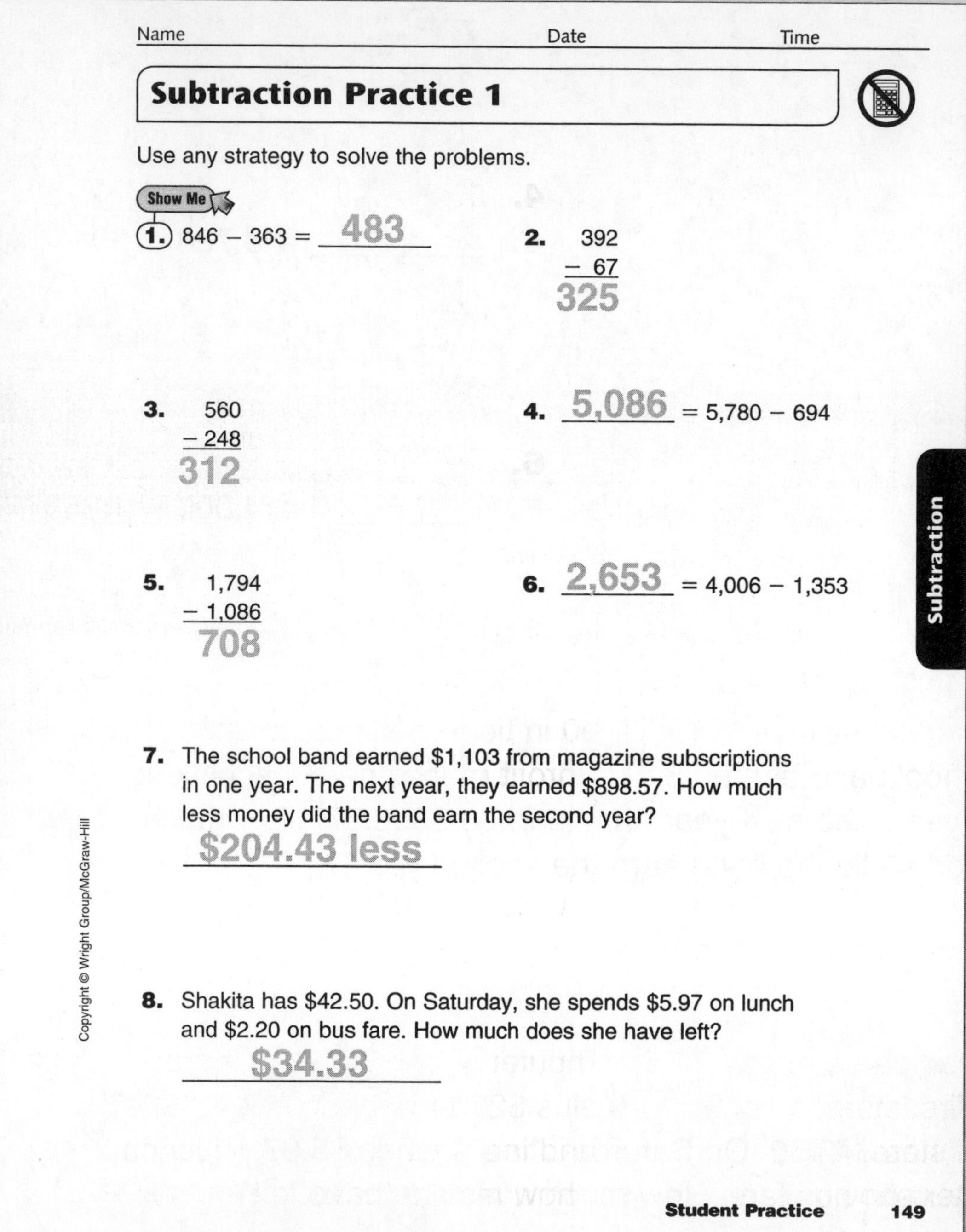

Name ______ Date ______ Time ______

Subtraction Practice 1

Use any strategy to solve the problems.

Show Me

1. 846 − 363 = 483

2. 392 − 67 = 325

3. 560 − 248 = 312

4. 5,086 = 5,780 − 694

5. 1,794 − 1,086 = 708

6. 2,653 = 4,006 − 1,353

7. The school band earned $1,103 from magazine subscriptions in one year. The next year, they earned $898.57. How much less money did the band earn the second year?
   $204.43 less

8. Shakita has $42.50. On Saturday, she spends $5.97 on lunch and $2.20 on bus fare. How much does she have left?
   $34.33

Name Date Time

Subtraction Practice 2

Use any strategy to solve the problems.

1. ________ = 7.83 − 2.89

2. 4.65 − 3.10 = ________

3. $\begin{array}{r} 6.80 \\ -\ 1.67 \\ \hline \end{array}$

4. 56.3 − 29.85 = ________

5. $\begin{array}{r} \$71.58 \\ -\ \$69.65 \\ \hline \end{array}$

6. $\begin{array}{r} 2 \\ -\ 1.85 \\ \hline \end{array}$

Subtraction

7. The school play takes in $893.90 in ticket sales. The play cost $213.87 to produce. How much profit did the school make?

____

8. Noah compares prices for a computer at two different stores. At the first store, it costs $680 plus $230 for a printer. At the second store, it costs $869.99 and includes a printer. Which computer should Noah buy and how much money will he save?

____

Answers to Subtraction Practice 2

While these problems may be appropriate for **fifth-grade** students, feel free to assign some or all of them to any student who needs practice at this level.

Recommended Use Use any time after Lesson 2-3 in Grade 5.

Name Date Time

Subtraction Practice 2

Use any strategy to solve the problems.

Show Me

1. 4.94 = 7.83 − 2.89

2. 4.65 − 3.10 = 1.55

3. 6.80 − 1.67 = 5.13

4. 56.3 − 29.85 = 26.45

5. $71.58 − $69.65 = $1.93

6. 2 − 1.85 = 0.15

7. The school play takes in $893.90 in ticket sales. The play cost $213.87 to produce. How much profit did the school make?
$680.03

8. Noah compares prices for a computer at two different stores. At the first store, it costs $680 plus $230 for a printer. At the second store, it costs $869.99 and includes a printer. Which computer should Noah buy and how much money will he save?
The computer from the second store; he will save $40.01.

Subtraction

Name ______ Date ______ Time ______

Addition and Subtraction Practice

Use any strategy to solve the problems.

Show Me

1. 7,945 + 8,438 = ______

2. $10.93 + $2.54

3. ______ = 22.9 − 10.49

4. 846 − 288

5. 1,097 + 672 + 185

6. 53.4 − 19.71

7. Raul has one board that is 3.15 meters long and another board that measures 6.8 meters. What is the difference in the lengths of the boards? ______

8. Shana and Gloria are linking daisy chains for the school's Fun Fair. One chain is 2.07 meters long. A second is 1.75 meters long, and the third measures 2.85 meters. How long is the final chain?

______

Addition

Subtraction

Answers to Addition and Subtraction Practice

While these problems may be appropriate for **fifth-grade** students, feel free to assign some or all of them to any student who needs practice at this level.

Recommended Use Use any time after Lesson 2-3 in Grade 5.

Addition

Subtraction

Name Date Time

Addition and Subtraction Practice

Use any strategy to solve the problems.

Show Me

1. 7,945 + 8,438 = 16,383

2. $10.93 + $2.54 = **$13.47**

3. 12.41 = 22.9 − 10.49

4. 846 − 288 = **558**

5. 1,097 + 672 + 185 = **1,954**

6. 53.4 − 19.71 = **33.69**

7. Raul has one board that is 3.15 meters long and another board that measures 6.8 meters. What is the difference in the lengths of the boards? **3.65 meters**

8. Shana and Gloria are linking daisy chains for the school's Fun Fair. One chain is 2.07 meters long. A second is 1.75 meters long, and the third measures 2.85 meters. How long is the final chain?
6.67 meters

Addition

Subtraction

Name ______________________ Date ______________ Time ______________

Multiplication Practice 1

Use any strategy to solve the problems.

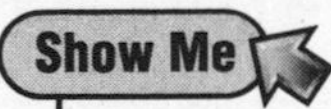

1. ________ = 42 × 37

2. 420
   ∗ 25

3. 80 ∗ 163 = ________

4. 2.2 ∗ 3.5 = ________

5. 300
   ∗ 67

6. 2.80
   ∗ 9.4

7. Max can mow 75 square feet of lawn per minute. How many square feet can he mow in an hour? ______________

8. The circus sells 245 sticks of cotton candy per show. Each stick sells for $2.25. How much will the circus make from cotton candy sales after 7 shows? ______________

Multiplication

Answers to Multiplication Practice 1

While these problems may be appropriate for **fifth-grade** students, feel free to assign some or all of them to any student who needs practice at this level.

Recommended Use Use any time after Lesson 2-8 in Grade 5.

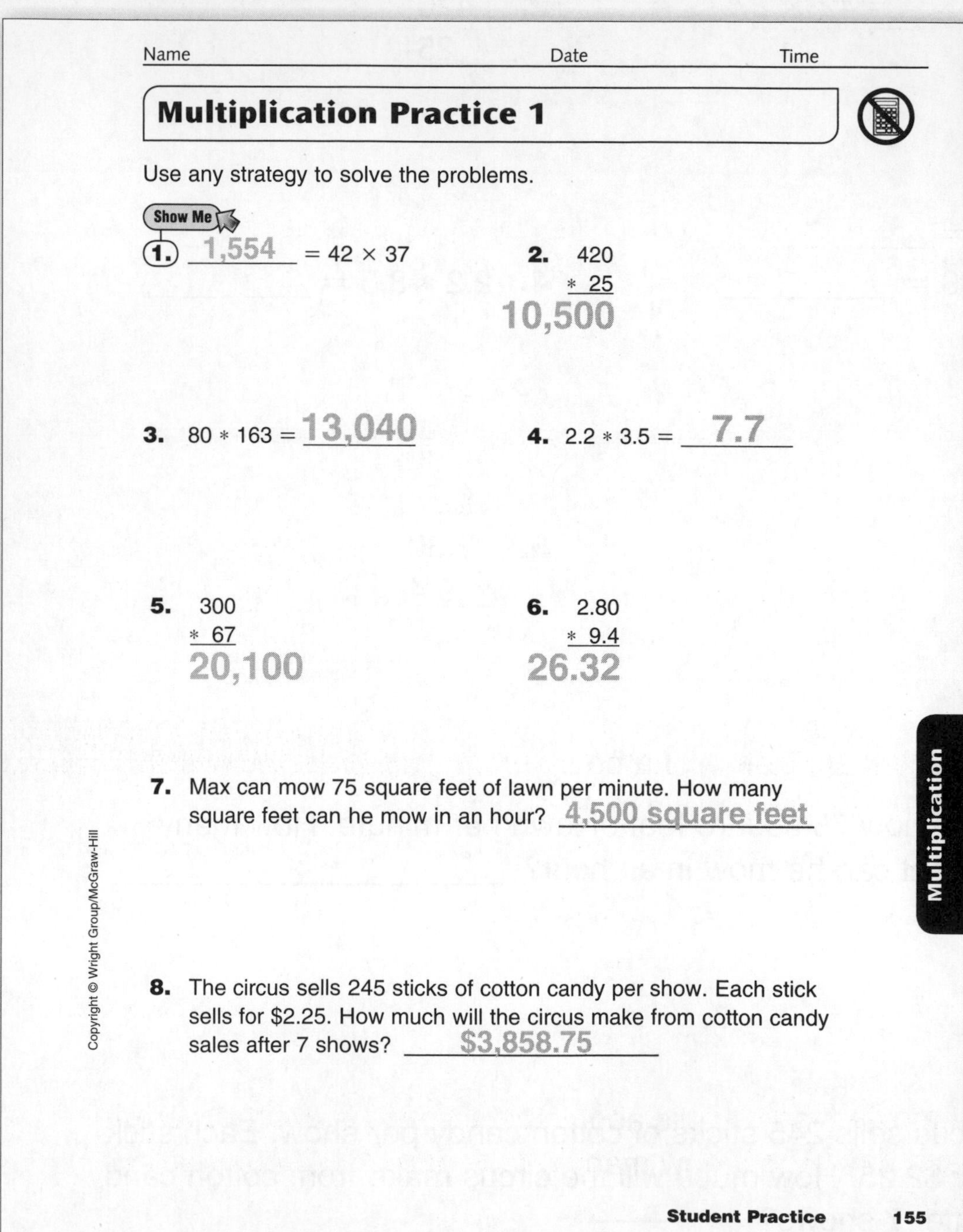

Name Date Time

Multiplication Practice 1

Use any strategy to solve the problems.

Show Me

1. 1,554 = 42 × 37

2. 420 * 25 = 10,500

3. 80 * 163 = 13,040

4. 2.2 * 3.5 = 7.7

5. 300 * 67 = 20,100

6. 2.80 * 9.4 = 26.32

7. Max can mow 75 square feet of lawn per minute. How many square feet can he mow in an hour? 4,500 square feet

8. The circus sells 245 sticks of cotton candy per show. Each stick sells for $2.25. How much will the circus make from cotton candy sales after 7 shows? $3,858.75

Multiplication

Student Practice 155

Multiplication

Name Date Time

Multiplication Practice 2

Use any strategy to solve the problems.

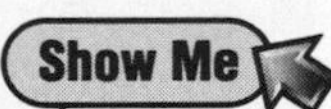

1. $43 \times 26 =$ ________

2. ________ $= 74 * 58$

3. $150 * 4 =$ ________

4. $0.71 \times 1.50 =$ ________

5. $\begin{array}{r} 2.9 \\ * \ 73 \\ \hline \end{array}$

6. $\begin{array}{r} 3.55 \\ * \ 1.7 \\ \hline \end{array}$

7. Derek can read one page of a book in 6.5 minutes. At this pace, how many pages will he read in 42 minutes?

____

8. The local movie theater sells about 125 boxes of yogurt-covered raisins each day. About how many boxes does the theater sell in one year? ________________

Multiplication

Answers to Multiplication Practice 2

While these problems may be appropriate for **fifth-grade** students, feel free to assign some or all of them to any student who needs practice at this level.

Recommended Use Use any time after Lesson 2-9 in Grade 5.

Name Date Time

Multiplication Practice 2

Use any strategy to solve the problems.

Show Me

1. 43 × 26 = **1,118**

2. **4,292** = 74 * 58

3. 150 * 4 = **600**

4. 0.71 × 1.50 = **1.065**

5. 2.9 * 73 = **211.7**

6. 3.55 * 1.7 = **6.035**

7. Derek can read one page of a book in 6.5 minutes. At this pace, how many pages will he read in 42 minutes?
273 pages

8. The local movie theater sells about 125 boxes of yogurt-covered raisins each day. About how many boxes does the theater sell in one year? **About 45,625 boxes**

Multiplication

Student Practice 157

Multiplication

Name Date Time

Division Practice 1

Use any strategy to solve the problems.

Show Me

1. 9427 / 7 = ________

2. $26\overline{)858}$

3. ________ = 429 ÷ 8

4. $20\overline{)688}$

5. ________ = 1,226/18

6. 3,978 ÷ 23 = ________

7. Kenneth passes out water during the baseball games. If the jug holds 640 ounces, how many 8 ounce glasses can he fill?

____

8. Katie has a photo that was enlarged 3 times its original size. The photo is now 10.5" × 13.5". What was the original size?

____

Answers to Division Practice 1

While these problems may be appropriate for **fifth-grade** students, feel free to assign some or all of them to any student who needs practice at this level.

Recommended Use Use any time after Lesson 4-2 in Grade 5.

Name Date Time

Division Practice 1

Use any strategy to solve the problems.

Show Me

1. 9427 / 7 = **1,346 R5**

2. 26)858 **33**

3. **53 R5** = 429 ÷ 8

4. 20)688 **34 R8**

5. **68 R2** = 1,226/18

6. 3,978 ÷ 23 = **172 R22**

7. Kenneth passes out water during the baseball games. If the jug holds 640 ounces, how many 8 ounce glasses can he fill?
80 glasses

8. Katie has a photo that was enlarged 3 times its original size. The photo is now 10.5" × 13.5". What was the original size?
3.5" × 4.5"

Division

Division

Name Date Time

Division Practice 2

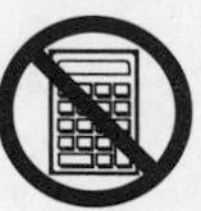

Use any strategy to solve the problems.

Show Me

1. 600 / 22 = ________

2. 363 ÷ 3

3. 895/26

4. $9\overline{)1{,}796}$

5. 2,856 ÷ 35

6. $72\overline{)9{,}628}$

7. Grace buys 11 packs of pencils for a total of $38.39. How much is each pack of pencils? ________________

8. There are 87 vitamins left in the bottle. If Joe takes 3 vitamins each day, how long will it be before he runs out of vitamins?

____

Division

Answers to Division Practice 2

While these problems may be appropriate for **fifth-grade** students, feel free to assign some or all of them to any student who needs practice at this level.

Recommended Use Use any time after Lesson 4-4 in Grade 5.

Name Date Time

Division Practice 2

Use any strategy to solve the problems.

Show Me

1. 600 / 22 = 27 R6
2. 363 ÷ 3 121
3. 895/26 34 R11
4. 9)1,796 196 R32
5. 2,856 ÷ 35 81 R21
6. 72)9,628 133 R52
7. Grace buys 11 packs of pencils for a total of $38.39. How much is each pack of pencils? $3.49
8. There are 87 vitamins left in the bottle. If Joe takes 3 vitamins each day, how long will it be before he runs out of vitamins? 29 days

Division

Division

Name Date Time

Multiplication and Division Practice

Use any strategy to solve the problems.

1. ________ = 9.29 × 5

2. 5.76 ÷ 3 = ________

3. $\begin{array}{r} 48.3 \\ \times\ 8.8 \\ \hline \end{array}$

4. $2\overline{)138.6}$

5. 63.9 ∗ 3.4 = ________

6. ________ = 2,975 / 3.5

7. The Randalls' yard measures 120 feet by 58 feet. What is the area of the yard? ________________

8. Rosita buys four new books for a total of $32.65. What is the average cost per book? ________________

Multiplication

Division

Answers to Multiplication and Division Practice

While these problems may be appropriate for **fifth-grade** students, feel free to assign some or all of them to any student who needs practice at this level.

Recommended Use Use any time after Lesson 4-5 in Grade 5.

Name _______________ Date _______________ Time _______________

Multiplication and Division Practice

Use any strategy to solve the problems.

Show Me

1. 46.45 = 9.29 × 5

2. 5.76 ÷ 3 = 1.92

3. 48.3 × 8.8 = 425.04

4. 2)138.6 = 69.3

5. 63.9 ∗ 3.4 = 217.26

6. 850 = 2,975 / 3.5

7. The Randalls' yard measures 120 feet by 58 feet. What is the area of the yard? 6,960 square feet

8. Rosita buys four new books for a total of $32.65. What is the average cost per book? $8.16

Multiplication

Division

Multiplication

Division

Name Date Time

Addition Practice

Use any strategy to solve the problems.

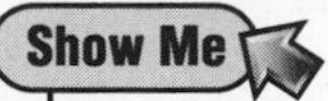

1. $4.56 + 7.9 =$ ________

2. $84.35 + 5.67$

3. $4.803 + 5.22$

4. ________ $= 61.79 + 3.772$

5. $36.991 + 2.704$

6. $52.671 + 90.432$

7. At the beginning of July, Trevor's car had 13,032.5 miles on the odometer. He drove 1,897.9 miles during the month. How many miles did the odometer show at the end of July? ____________

8. During a science experiment, Melinda mixes 687.083 milliliters of water with 502.66 milliliters of vinegar. How much liquid is in her measuring cup? ____________

Answers to Addition Practice

While these problems may be appropriate for **sixth-grade** students, feel free to assign some or all of them to any student who needs practice at this level.

Recommended Use Use any time after Lesson 2-3 in Grade 6.

Addition

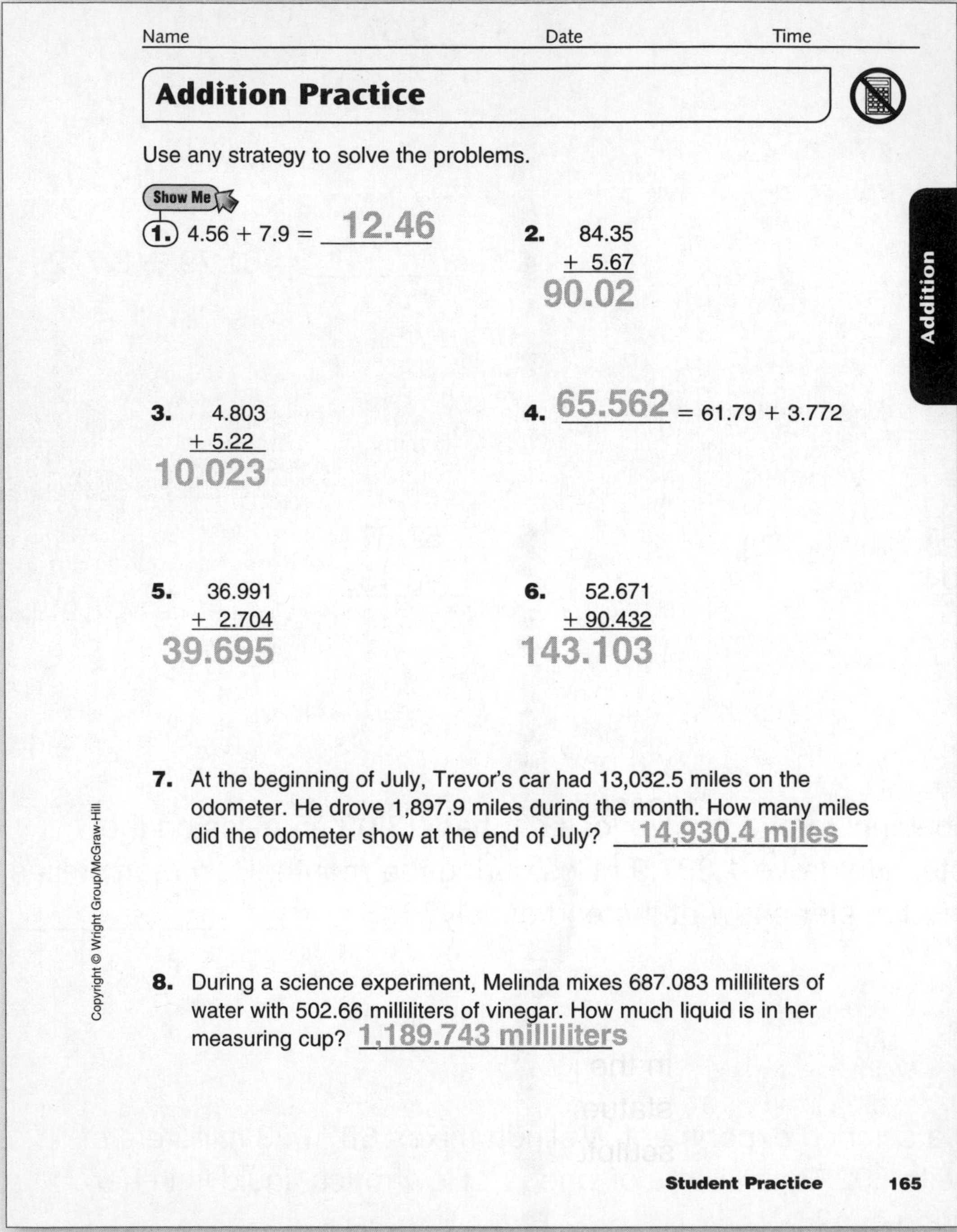

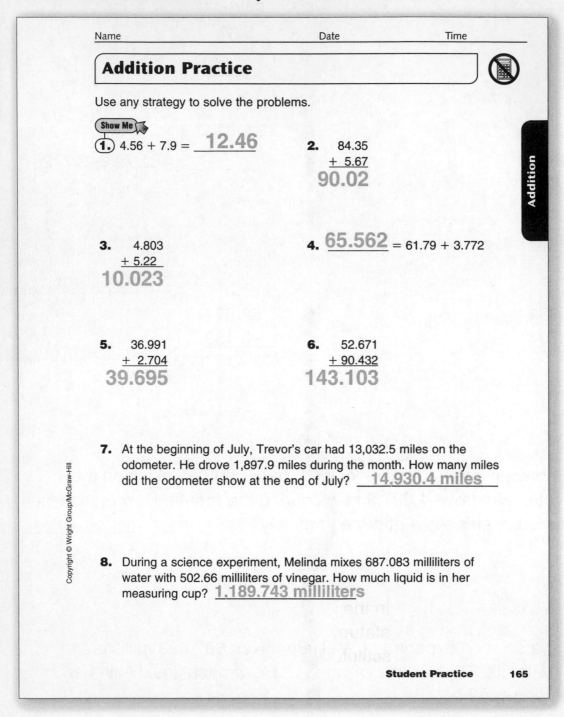

Name Date Time

Addition Practice

Use any strategy to solve the problems.

Show Me

1. 4.56 + 7.9 = 12.46

2. 84.35 + 5.67 = 90.02

3. 4.803 + 5.22 = 10.023

4. 65.562 = 61.79 + 3.772

5. 36.991 + 2.704 = 39.695

6. 52.671 + 90.432 = 143.103

7. At the beginning of July, Trevor's car had 13,032.5 miles on the odometer. He drove 1,897.9 miles during the month. How many miles did the odometer show at the end of July? 14,930.4 miles

8. During a science experiment, Melinda mixes 687.083 milliliters of water with 502.66 milliliters of vinegar. How much liquid is in her measuring cup? 1,189.743 milliliters

Addition

Name Date Time

Subtraction Practice

Use any strategy to solve the problems.

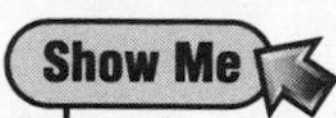

1. ________ = 6.52 − 3.74

2. 33.29 − 26.87 = ________

3. $\begin{array}{r} 5.391 \\ -\ 3.456 \\ \hline \end{array}$

4. 5.06 − 3.49 = ________

5. $\begin{array}{r} 8.05 \\ -\ 5.894 \\ \hline \end{array}$

6. $\begin{array}{r} 85.100 \\ -\ 36.71 \\ \hline \end{array}$

7. Sean needs $56.34 to buy a new skateboard. He has $36.77. How much more does he need? ________________

8. An artist built a sculpture in the park that measured 55.133 meters. Across the square was a statue that measured 46.882 meters. How much taller was the sculpture than the statue?

____

Subtraction

Answers to Subtraction Practice

While these problems may be appropriate for **sixth-grade** students, feel free to assign some or all of them to any student who needs practice at this level.

Recommended Use Use any time after Lesson 2-3 in Grade 6.

Subtraction

Name Date Time

Subtraction Practice

Use any strategy to solve the problems.

Show Me

1. 2.78 = 6.52 − 3.74

2. 33.29 − 26.87 = 6.42

3. 5.391 − 3.456 = 1.935

4. 5.06 − 3.49 = 1.57

5. 8.05 − 5.894 = 2.156

6. 85.100 − 36.71 = 48.39

7. Sean needs $56.34 to buy a new skateboard. He has $36.77. How much more does he need? $19.57

8. An artist built a sculpture in the park that measured 55.133 meters. Across the square was a statue that measured 46.882 meters. How much taller was the sculpture than the statue?

8.251 meters

Subtraction

Student Practice 167

Name ________________ Date ________________ Time ________________

Addition and Subtraction Practice

Use any strategy to solve the problems.

1. ________ = 32.5 + 19.6

2. 6.7 − 4.892 = ________

3.
```
  62.80
+  3.69
```

4.
```
  5.08
− 2.94
```

5.
```
  35.976
+ 83.79
```

6.
```
  53.004
− 21.007
```

7. A frog hops 2.077 meters on its first hop. On its second hop, it hops 2.93 meters. How many meters did it hop altogether?

____

8. LeToya's mother buys 4.5 yards of fabric. She makes a dress and uses 2.6 yards. How much fabric does she have left?

____

Addition

Subtraction

Answers to Addition and Subtraction Practice

While these problems may be appropriate for **sixth-grade** students, feel free to assign some or all of them to any student who needs practice at this level.

Recommended Use Use any time after Lesson 2-3 in Grade 6.

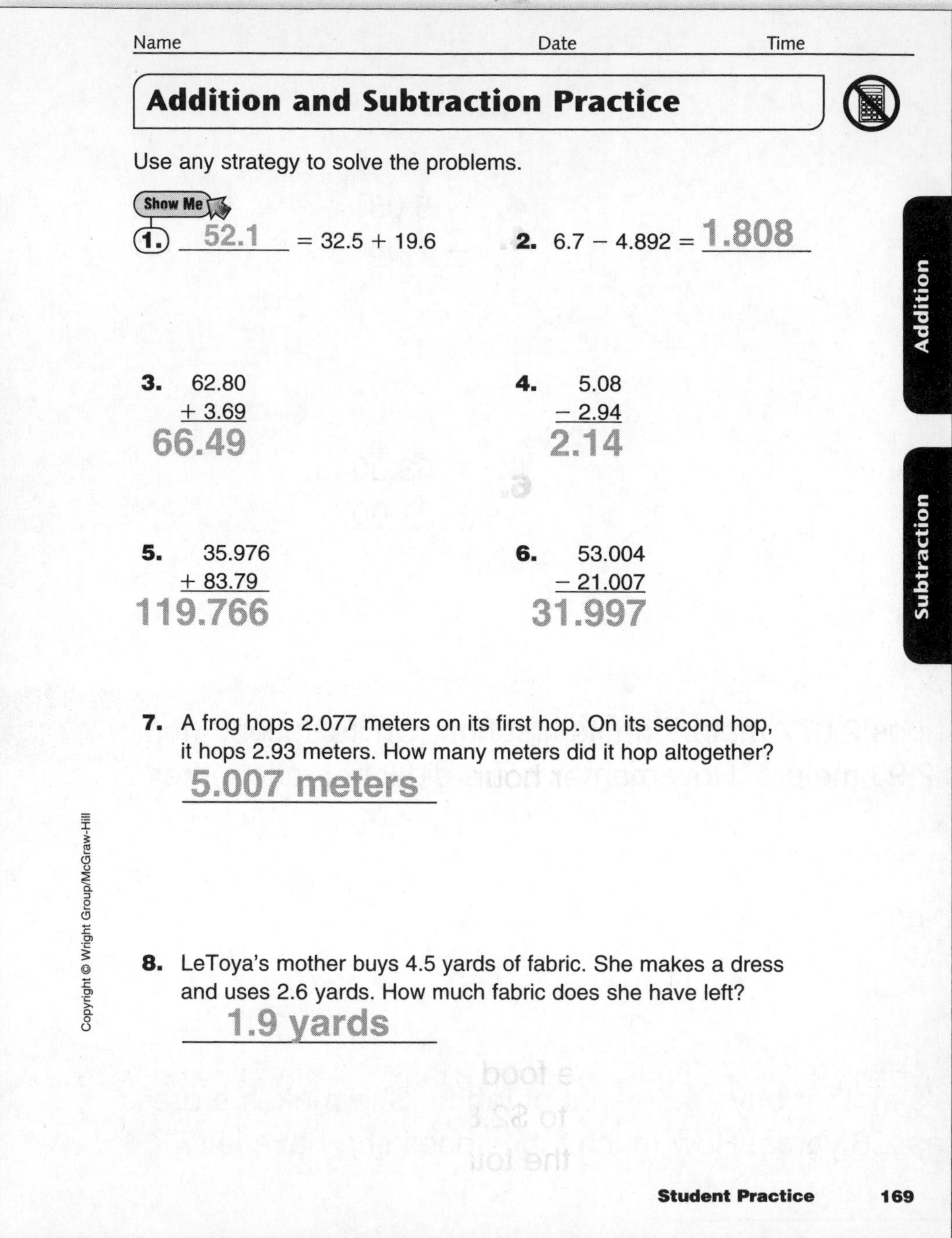

Name Date Time

Addition and Subtraction Practice

Use any strategy to solve the problems.

Show Me

1. 52.1 = 32.5 + 19.6

2. 6.7 − 4.892 = 1.808

3. 62.80 + 3.69 = 66.49

4. 5.08 − 2.94 = 2.14

5. 35.976 + 83.79 = 119.766

6. 53.004 − 21.007 = 31.997

7. A frog hops 2.077 meters on its first hop. On its second hop, it hops 2.93 meters. How many meters did it hop altogether?
5.007 meters

8. LeToya's mother buys 4.5 yards of fabric. She makes a dress and uses 2.6 yards. How much fabric does she have left?
1.9 yards

Name Date Time

Multiplication Practice 1

Use any strategy to solve the problems.

Show Me

1. $6 * 4.79 =$ ________

2. ________ $= 4 * 3.8$

3. $7.3 * 9.2 =$ ________

4. ________ $= 8.1 * 3.9$

5. $13 * 2.78 =$ ________

6. $\begin{array}{r} 5.7 \\ * \ 31 \\ \hline \end{array}$

7. If a train travels at 67.6 miles per hour, how far will it go in 12 hours?

____

8. For the Spanish Club dinner, the food bill was $493.99, and the cups, plates and silverware added up to $2.89 per person. If 298 people attended the dinner, what were the total expenses?

____

Multiplication

Answers to Multiplication Practice 1

While these problems may be appropriate for **sixth-grade** students, feel free to assign some or all of them to any student who needs practice at this level.

Recommended Use Use any time after Lesson 2-5 in Grade 6.

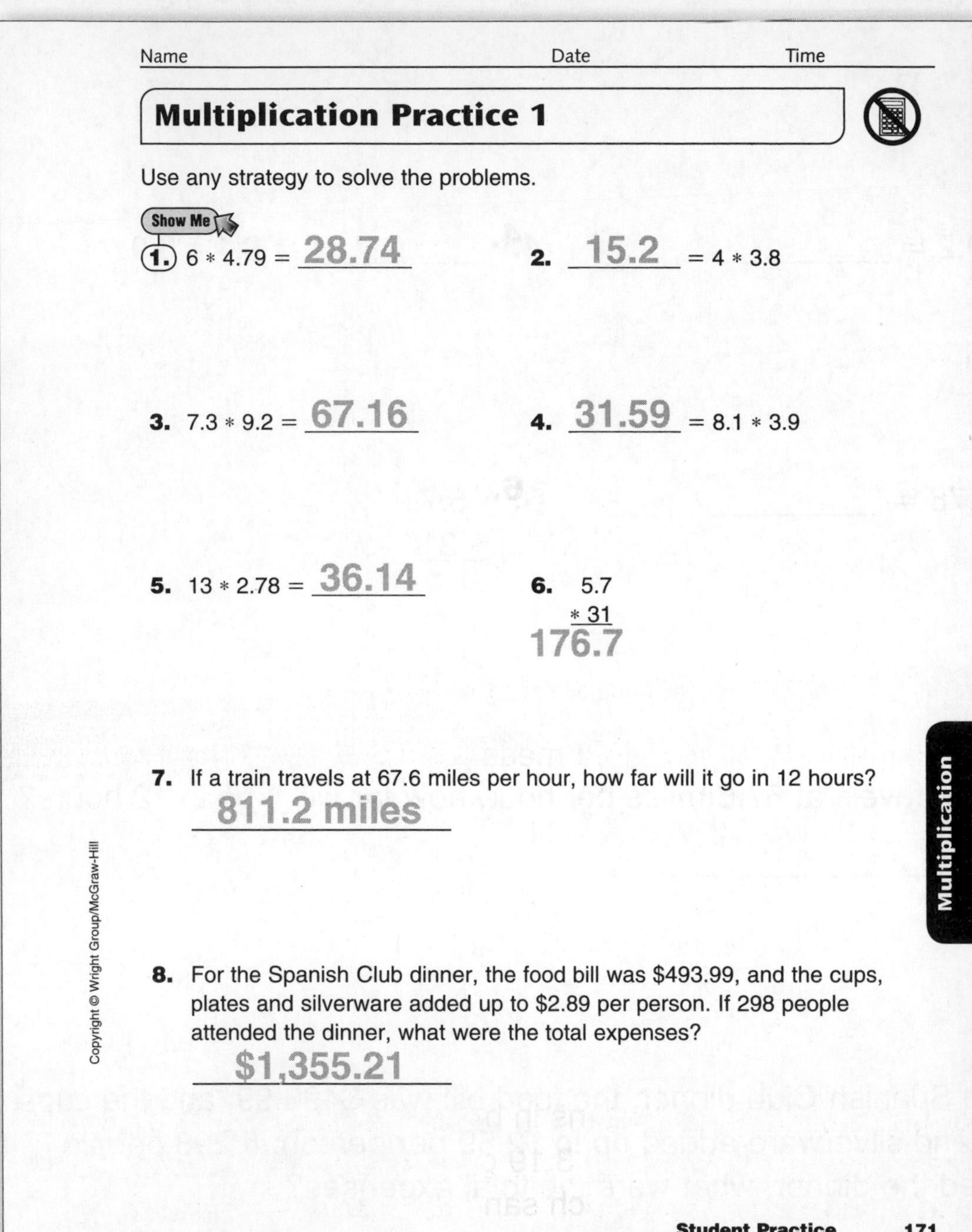

Name Date Time

Multiplication Practice 1

Use any strategy to solve the problems.

Show Me

1. 6 * 4.79 = 28.74
2. 15.2 = 4 * 3.8
3. 7.3 * 9.2 = 67.16
4. 31.59 = 8.1 * 3.9
5. 13 * 2.78 = 36.14
6. 5.7 * 31 = 176.7
7. If a train travels at 67.6 miles per hour, how far will it go in 12 hours? 811.2 miles
8. For the Spanish Club dinner, the food bill was $493.99, and the cups, plates and silverware added up to $2.89 per person. If 298 people attended the dinner, what were the total expenses? $1,355.21

Multiplication

Multiplication

Name Date Time

Multiplication Practice 2

Use any strategy to solve the problems.

Show Me

1. 45.5 * 3.06 = __________

2. __________ = 14.6 × 0.2

3. 741 * 3.6 = __________

4. __________ = 25.80 * 0.81

5. 3.53 * 4.4 = __________

6. 597.2
× 8.1

7. What is the area of a scarf that measures .833 m by .254 m?

____

8. Shondra is making sand designs in bottles. For each of 3 bottles, she needs blue sand weighing 3.19 grams, and yellow sand weighing 4.59 grams. How much sand does she need in all?

____

Multiplication

Answers to Multiplication Practice 2

While these problems may be appropriate for **sixth-grade** students, feel free to assign some or all of them to any student who needs practice at this level.

Recommended Use Use after Lesson 2-6 in Grade 6.

Name ________ Date ________ Time ________

Multiplication Practice 2

Use any strategy to solve the problems.

Show Me

1. 45.5 * 3.06 = **139.23**
2. **2.92** = 14.6 × 0.2
3. 741 * 3.6 = **2,667.6**
4. **20.898** = 25.80 * 0.81
5. 3.53 * 4.4 = **15.532**
6. 597.2 × 8.1 = **4,837.32**
7. What is the area of a scarf that measures .833 m by .254 m? **.211582 m^2**
8. Shondra is making sand designs in bottles. For each of 3 bottles, she needs blue sand weighing 3.19 grams, and yellow sand weighing 4.59 grams. How much sand does she need in all? **23.34 grams**

Multiplication

Student Practice 173

Multiplication

Name Date Time

Division Practice 1

Use any strategy to solve the problems.

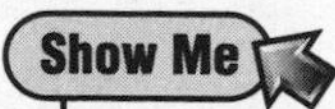

1. 800 / 22 = ________

2. ________ = 448 / 16

3. $12\overline{)624}$

4. ________ = 587 ÷ 38

5. $42\overline{)1{,}587}$

6. 4,889 ÷ 18 = ________

7. Megan's dad's printer can print 3 pages per minute. About how long will it take to print Megan's 55-page report?

____

8. A total of 2,480 students take the bus to school. Each school bus holds 35 students. How many buses does the school need?

____

Answers to Division Practice 1

While these problems may be appropriate for **sixth-grade** students, feel free to assign some or all of them to any student who needs practice at this level.

Recommended Use Use any time after Lesson 2-7 in Grade 6.

Name ____________________ Date __________ Time __________

Division Practice 1

Use any strategy to solve the problems.

Show Me

1. 800 / 22 = 36 R8

2. 28 = 448 / 16

3. 12)624 — 52

4. 15 R17 = 587 ÷ 38

5. 42)1,587 — 37 R33

6. 4,889 ÷ 18 = 271 R11

7. Megan's dad's printer can print 3 pages per minute. About how long will it take to print Megan's 55-page report?
   About 18 or 19 minutes

8. A total of 2,480 students take the bus to school. Each school bus holds 35 students. How many buses does the school need?
   70 R30 or 71 buses

Division

Division

Name Date Time

Division Practice 2

Use any strategy to solve the following problems.

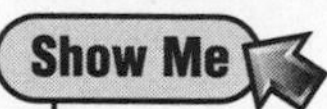

1. ________ = 381 / 4

2. $12\overline{)498}$

3. $5\overline{)12.8}$

4. 573.1 ÷ 11 = ________

5. ________ = 108.36 / 9

6. 89.88 ÷12 = ________

7. Clara walks 8 blocks to the store. It takes her 10.4 minutes to walk the distance. How long does it take her to walk one block?

____

8. Anthony earns $156.88 for mowing lawns over the summer. He decides to share it equally with his brother and sister, who sometimes help him. How much does each person get?

____

Answers to Division Practice 2

While these problems may be appropriate for **sixth-grade** students, feel free to assign some or all of them to any student who needs practice at this level.

Recommended Use Use after Lesson 2-8 in Grade 6.

Name ____________________ Date __________ Time __________

Division Practice 2

Use any strategy to solve the following problems.

Show Me

1. 95.25 = 381 / 4
2. 12)498 — 41.5 or 41 R6
3. 5)12.8 — 2.56
4. 573.1 ÷ 11 = 52.1
5. 12.04 = 108.36 / 9
6. 89.88 ÷ 12 = 7.49
7. Clara walks 8 blocks to the store. It takes her 10.4 minutes to walk the distance. How long does it take her to walk one block?
   1.3 minutes
8. Anthony earns $156.88 for mowing lawns over the summer. He decides to share it equally with his brother and sister, who sometimes help him. How much does each person get?
   $52.29 (R1)

Division

Division

Name Date Time

Multiplication and Division Practice 1

Use any strategy to solve the problems.

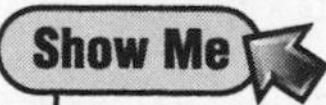

1. 1,010 / 6 = ________

2. ________ = 5,495 ÷ 14

3. 5)671

4. 2,148 ∗ 13 = ________

5. 33 ∗ 3,485 = ________

6. ________ = 219 / 12

7. The area of a tile floor is 54 ft^2. If the floor is 8 ft long, what is the width of the floor? ________________

8. A school survey indicates that the average student has 5 notebooks in his or her desk. If there are 427 students in the school, about how many notebooks are there altogether? ________________

Multiplication

Division

Answers to Multiplication and Division Practice 1

While these problems may be appropriate for **sixth-grade** students, feel free to assign some or all of them to any student who needs practice at this level.

Recommended Use Use any time after Lesson 2-7 in Grade 6.

Name Date Time

Multiplication and Division Practice 1

Use any strategy to solve the problems.

1. 1,010 / 6 = 168 R2
2. 392.5 = 5,495 ÷ 14
3. 5)671 134.2
4. 2,148 * 13 = 27,924
5. 33 * 3,485 = 115,005
6. 18.25 = 219 / 12
7. The area of a tile floor is 54 ft^2. If the floor is 8 ft long, what is the width of the floor? 7 ft
8. A school survey indicates that the average student has 5 notebooks in his or her desk. If there are 427 students in the school, about how many notebooks are there altogether? 2,135 notebooks

Multiplication Division

Multiplication Division

Name Date Time

Multiplication and Division Practice 2

Use any strategy to solve the following problems.

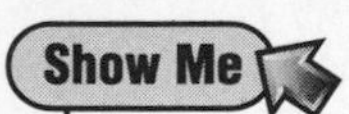

1. ________ = 37.2 / 3

2. 5 * 10.844 = ________

3. 170.4 ÷ 12 = ________

4. $23\overline{)2{,}991.84}$

5. ________ = 2.2 * 113

6. $\begin{array}{r} 19.2 \\ \times\ 6.4 \\ \hline \end{array}$

7. Marisol and her friends Juanita and Angela drive to another city for a swim meet. She spends $46.76 to fill up her car with gas. Her friends offer to split the cost of the gas. How much does each girl owe?

____

8. Find the area of a rectangle with a length of .687 mm and a width of .038 mm. ________________

Multiplication

Division

Answers to Multiplication and Division Practice 2

While these problems may be appropriate for **sixth-grade** students, feel free to assign some or all of them to any student who needs practice at this level.

Recommended Use Use any time after Lesson 2-8 in Grade 6.

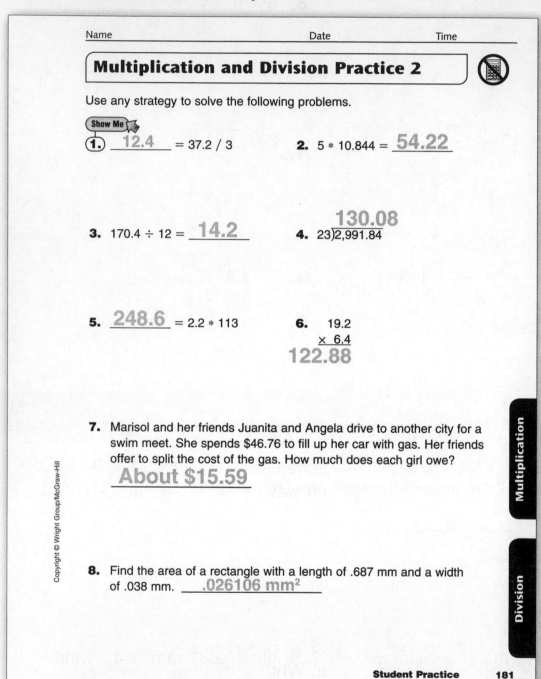

Name ______ Date ______ Time ______

Multiplication and Division Practice 2

Use any strategy to solve the following problems.

Show Me

1. 12.4 = 37.2 / 3
2. 5 * 10.844 = 54.22
3. 170.4 ÷ 12 = 14.2
4. 23)2,991.84 — 130.08
5. 248.6 = 2.2 * 113
6. 19.2 × 6.4 = 122.88
7. Marisol and her friends Juanita and Angela drive to another city for a swim meet. She spends $46.76 to fill up her car with gas. Her friends offer to split the cost of the gas. How much does each girl owe?
   About $15.59
8. Find the area of a rectangle with a length of .687 mm and a width of .038 mm. .026106 mm^2

Multiplication

Division

Multiplication

Division

Name Date Time

Multiplication and Division Practice 3

Use any strategy to solve the problems.

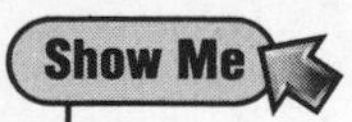

1. ________ = 45.5 * 3.06

2. 5)19.2

3. 40.70
   * 1.7

4. 28.3 × 8.71 = ________

5. 373.56 ÷ 66 = ________

6. ________ = 127.8 / 20

7. At age one, Finn's little sister weighed 18.75 pounds. This is 2.5 times her weight at birth. What was her birth weight?

____

8. Monique's picture is 8.4 in. × 10.3 in. She wants to make the picture 3 times larger for a poster. What will be the dimensions of the larger picture? ________________

Multiplication

Division

Answers to Multiplication and Division Practice 3

While these problems may be appropriate for **sixth-grade** students, feel free to assign some or all of them to any student who needs practice at this level.

Recommended Use Use any time after Lesson 2-8 in Grade 6.

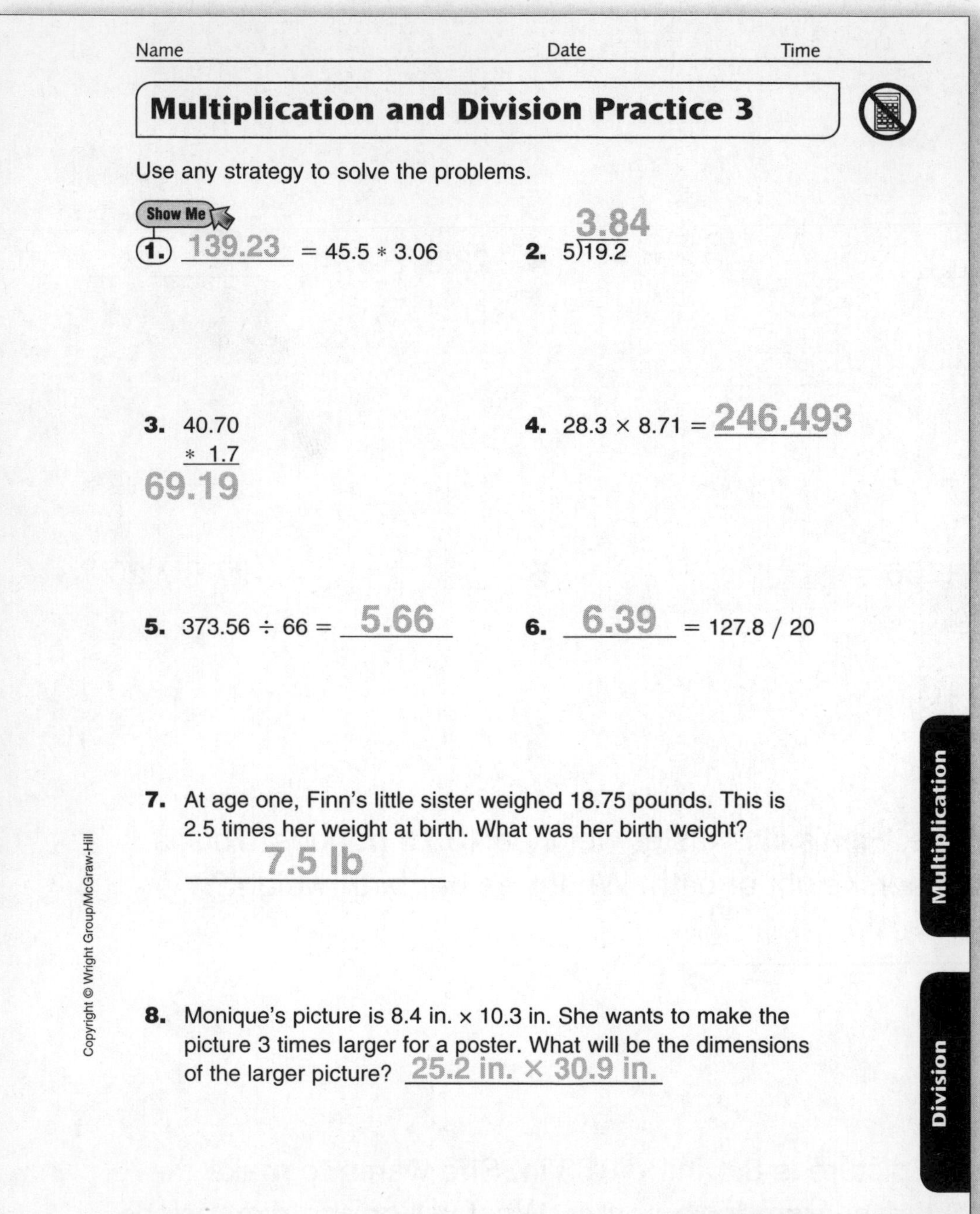

Name Date Time

Multiplication and Division Practice 3

Use any strategy to solve the problems.

Show Me

1. 139.23 = 45.5 ∗ 3.06

2. 5)19.2 — 3.84

3. 40.70 ∗ 1.7 = 69.19

4. 28.3 × 8.71 = 246.493

5. 373.56 ÷ 66 = 5.66

6. 6.39 = 127.8 / 20

7. At age one, Finn's little sister weighed 18.75 pounds. This is 2.5 times her weight at birth. What was her birth weight?
7.5 lb

8. Monique's picture is 8.4 in. × 10.3 in. She wants to make the picture 3 times larger for a poster. What will be the dimensions of the larger picture? 25.2 in. × 30.9 in.

Multiplication

Division

Student Practice 183

Multiplication

Division